CORE COMMUNICATION

Maps, Skills, and Processes

Sherod Miller, Ph.D.

Phyllis A. Miller, Ph.D.

Second Edition
Printed in Canada
Cover design: Barrie Maguire

TYRO SUPPORT SERVICES

J169 State Route 65
McClure, OH 43534
Toll Free: 800-328-5099
www.comskills.com

PREFACE

Purpose
Ground Rules
Materials

The purpose of this workbook is to help enhance your interpersonal competence — your knowledge of and skill in communication, to:

- Develop greater choice in how you relate
- Talk and listen more effectively
- Make better decisions
- Resolve issues and conflicts better — both inside yourself and with others
- Coach or facilitate others in resolving issues or conflicts

Achieving increased interpersonal competence will enable you to:

- Create more satisfying relationships
- Expand your options for meeting and handling personal challenges
- Lower your level of stress
- Improve productivity when a task is involved that includes other people

In addition, you will be better personally and professionally at:

- Influencing
- Mediating
- Negotiating
- Counseling

GROUND RULES

As you learn the skills and processes in this material, keep the following ground rules in mind:

- *Participate voluntarily* in any activity (exercise) or discussion. If for any reason you do not choose to participate, say so. You can pass.

- *Respect boundaries.* Every person has his or her own informational boundaries. Take your own and others' into account. To do this:

  1. Identify or choose issues you think are appropriate to talk about in this setting.

  2. Do not pressure anyone else to disclose anything he or she does not wish to disclose.

- *Choose real issues* as you focus on skill practice. It is best to start with smaller issues instead of major ones as you learn the skills and processes.

- *Assume you will be coached* by the instructor and others in the class. Coaching and receiving feedback are essential for skill learning.

MATERIALS

Each participant uses one set of materials. Two versions include:

- Core Pac — Small, which contains:

  - This workbook, CORE COMMUNICATION: MAPS, SKILLS, AND PROCESSES

  - One Tabletop/Laptop Skills Mat

  - One Pocket Card Set

  - One Awareness Wheel Pad

- Core Pac — Large, which contains:

  - This workbook, CORE COMMUNICATION: MAPS, SKILLS, AND PROCESSES

  - One Awareness Wheel Floor Skills Mat

  - One Listening Cycle Floor Skills Mat

  - One Tabletop/Laptop Skills Mat

  - One Pocket Card Set

  - One Awareness Wheel Pad

CONTENTS

Contents

HOW DO I COMMUNICATE?

Date _____

Instructions: Take this Pre-Questionnaire to reflect on how you communicate. The questions relate to the skills and processes taught in CORE COMMUNICATION. Please follow the four steps below. Then set your learning goals on page x.

Step 1. Mark each item twice: first with an "X" to represent your typical behavior and again with an "O" to represent your more-so or less-so desired behavior. If your typical and desired behaviors are the same, the "X" and "O" marks will be on the same number. If they are not the same, the marks will fall on different numbers.

In general, when you are discussing an important issue with someone, how often do you:

	Seldom Often	Difference
1. Attempt to avoid the the issue by joking or changing the subject?	1 2 3 4 5 6	____
2. Listen briefly, then begin talking?	1 2 3 4 5 6	____
3. Speak for other — put words into the other person's mouth?	1 2 3 4 5 6	____
4. Direct or instruct the other in what to do about it?	1 2 3 4 5 6	____
5. Insist on "my way or the highway?"	1 2 3 4 5 6	____
6. Blame or attack the other person directly?	1 2 3 4 5 6	____
7. Make spiteful, undercutting remarks indirectly?	1 2 3 4 5 6	____
8. Withhold or misrepresent information?	1 2 3 4 5 6	____
9. Realize you are being ineffective?	1 2 3 4 5 6	____
10. Calm yourself consciously when you feel tense or encounter tension in the other?	1 2 3 4 5 6	____
11. Recognize what is going on inside yourself?	1 2 3 4 5 6	____
12. Own your behavior — your contribution or response to situation?	1 2 3 4 5 6	____
13. Describe your observations?	1 2 3 4 5 6	____
14. Express your thoughts?	1 2 3 4 5 6	____
15. Share your emotions?	1 2 3 4 5 6	____
16. Disclose your wants and desires?	1 2 3 4 5 6	____
17. Commit to future action(s)?	1 2 3 4 5 6	____

Pre-Questionnaire

	Seldom	Often	Difference
18. Attend to the other's nonverbal responses?	1 2 3 4 5 6		___
19. Establish and maintain rapport?	1 2 3 4 5 6		___
20. Ask what is going on inside the other person?	1 2 3 4 5 6		___
21. Acknowledge the other's emotions?	1 2 3 4 5 6		___
22. Invite/encourage the other to talk?	1 2 3 4 5 6		___
23. Summarize the other's perspective accurately?	1 2 3 4 5 6		___
24. Identify clearly what the issue is before discussing it?	1 2 3 4 5 6		___
25. Propose a good time and place to discuss the issue?	1 2 3 4 5 6		___
26. Begin a discussion without considering the other's readiness?	1 2 3 4 5 6		___
27. Decide on a solution before fully understanding the issue?	1 2 3 4 5 6		___
28. Talk about the issue but leave it unresolved?	1 2 3 4 5 6		___
29. Give in to the other to keep the peace?	1 2 3 4 5 6		___
30. Follow an effective process for resolving issues?	1 2 3 4 5 6		___
31. Explore possible causes of the issue?	1 2 3 4 5 6		___
32. Brainstorm solutions to the issue?	1 2 3 4 5 6		___
33. Settle the issue by compromising — trading something for something?	1 2 3 4 5 6		___
34. Build in the wants and interests of the other?	1 2 3 4 5 6		___
35. Resolve the issue by building agreements collaboratively?	1 2 3 4 5 6		___
36. Make sure a solution to the issue fits well for everyone involved?	1 2 3 4 5 6		___

Total Difference Score   ___

Step 2. When you have completed marking all the items, calculate the numerical difference between typical and desired scores for each item and record the results in the "difference" column. If the "X" and "O" are on the same number, the difference = 0. If the "X" is on 5 and the "O" is on 2, the difference = 3. Note that the "O" can be located on a higher or lower number than the "X." Do not be concerned about the higher or lower direction of the scores, just calculate the numerical difference between the marks.

Step 3. Sum the difference scores.

(Continue to next page)

Step 4. Look over the Questionnaire and put a check mark next to each item number (to the left of a question) with a difference score of "2" or more. These relate to skills and processes most beneficial for you to develop or change. Then set your learning goals.

MY LEARNING GOALS

Instructions: From the items you checked on the Pre-Questionnaire (see Step 4 above), write five behaviors you want to increase or decrease. Consider these as your major learning goals.

Goals: **Brief description of behavior to increase or decrease:**

1. Item # ___   _____

2. Item # ___   _____

3. Item # ___   _____

4. Item # ___   _____

5. Item # ___   _____

After the course, take the Post-Questionnaire on page 192, to compare your change.

WORKSHEET: SOMEONE I WANT TO INFLUENCE

Instructions: Think of a person you want to influence about something of importance to you. Take four minutes, and in the space below, organize what you want to say to this person.

Person's name:_____

Later you will return to this page.

INTRODUCTION

Your SOS Networks
Assumption in CORE
Communication: Behavior & Attitude

YOUR SOS NETWORKS

Most of us live and connect with others in relationship networks — various sub-systems of family, friends, neighbors, and colleagues or associates at work, school, and elsewhere. Also, most of us want to communicate effectively and have good relationships. This is especially so when we make a decision or when an issue arises, because such situations usually involve other people in some way. SOS represents the people that a particular issue involves or affects in your network: S stands for self, O for other(s), and S for stakeholders, as described in the chart below.

S	O	S
Self	**Other(s)**	**Stakeholders**
Yourself	People who are *immediately/ centrally* involved	People who are *peripherally* involved yet still affected

SOS helps you think systemically about the people in your sphere of communication. The SOS acronym suggests that a change in one person or part of your network, in regard to an issue, affects the whole relationship system. It is like a ripple effect in water — what happens in one part changes the surrounding area, as well.

THINK SYSTEMS — PARTS AND WHOLE

Consider these points about your SOS system of relationships:

- People are often interconnected and interdependent.

- When making a decision about an issue, other parts of your SOS system are impacted, too.

- Depending on your conversation with a person regarding an issue, someone can shift from "other" to "stakeholder" (or vice versa). For example:

    You and a sibling are in conflict regarding a situation with a parent. When you talk with your sibling, he or she is the "other," and your parent and possibly more family members are the stakeholders. When you interact with your parent, your sibling may become a stakeholder.

- By yourself, altering your communication can make a difference for others, as well.

ASSUMPTION IN CORE COMMUNICATION

The points given above from systems thinking lead to the following assumption:

IT TAKES ONE PERSON

It only takes one person to change an interaction. (Many people wait for and hope someone else will change, in order to improve their communication. This usually means no change occurs.)

The assumption in this workbook is that you, on your own, can effectively apply skills and processes to influence your interactions positively, even if others do not know the skills.

COMMUNICATION — BEHAVIOR AND ATTITUDE

Every message you communicate contains two parts:

> **Behavior** — Observable words and actions.
>
> **Attitude** — The mental view you hold, which comes from a combination of your beliefs, emotions, and intentions.

Behavior

Your words and actions — both verbal and non-verbal that are heard and seen by others — influence:

- How you come across to others
- How they respond to you

Attitude

The attitudes most important to your communication behavior revolve around caring or uncaring:

- Caring — valuing, respecting, or taking into account (counting), shown with arrow pointing up.
- Uncaring — not valuing, not respecting, or not taking into account (discounting), shown with arrow pointing down.

These attitudes represent your momentary or long-term assumptions about your own or someone else's significance. You express one of these two attitudes:

I don't care about (do not value or respect — I discount) . . .

I care about (value or respect — I count) . . .

In an interaction, your behavior demonstrates either that you do not care about yourself or the other person, or that you do.

I Do Not Care About Me When I *(Discount Me)*:

- Avoid Issues/Conflict

- Deceive myself — deny, disregard my own awareness

- Disown responsibility for my contributions and responses

- Withhold awareness or disclose awareness inappropriately

- Send confusing messages

- Make poor decisions

- Do not ask for/Refuse help when needed

- Fail to exercise my talents and acknowledge my limitations

- Deflect praise, appreciation, and recognition

- Act out of compulsion/anger

- Believe I am a victim and let others walk over me — shrink from action

I Care About Me When I *(Count Me)*:

- Face Issues/Conflict

- Expand and accept my own awareness

- Take responsibility for my own decisions and actions

- Disclose awareness appropriately

- Send clear messages

- Make good decisions

- Ask for/Accept help when needed

- Realize my strengths and limitations

- Accept praise, appreciation, and recognition

- Act out of choice

- Believe I am an agent and stand up for myself — take action

Introduction

I Do Not Care About You When I *(Discount You):*

- Ignore your concerns and interests

- Miss your non-verbal cues

- Deny your difference

- Disregard my impact on you

- Blame you for my actions

- Claim your accomplishments as my own

- Withhold praise, appreciation and recognition when warranted

- Refuse to help

- Seek control rather than understanding and cooperation

- Force agreements

- Walk over you and put you down

I Care About You When I *(Count You):*

- Attend to your concerns and interests

- Notice your non-verbal cues

- Acknowledge your difference

- Recognize my impact on you

- Own my own actions

- Enjoy your accomplishments as yours

- Give praise, appreciation and recognition when warranted

- Give help

- Cooperate rather than control

- Build agreements

- Respect you as a person

DISCOUNTING AND COUNTING SELF AND OTHER(S)

Instructions

Use the items listed on the previous pages (pages 4 - 5) to fill in the four boxes below. For the "other," consider someone you relate to on a regular basis, such as family, friend, or co-worker.

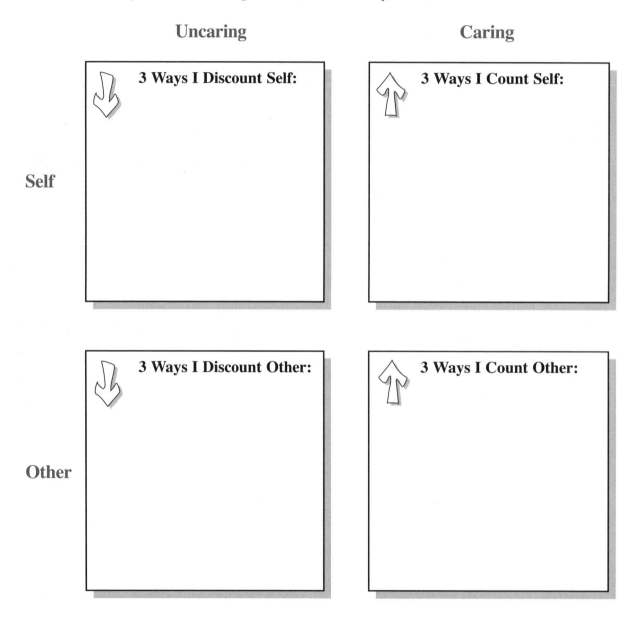

	Uncaring	Caring
Self	⬇ 3 Ways I Discount Self:	⬆ 3 Ways I Count Self:
Other	⬇ 3 Ways I Discount Other:	⬆ 3 Ways I Count Other:

ATTITUDE IS A CHOICE

The choice is always yours to communicate, either "I don't care . . ." or "I care . . ."

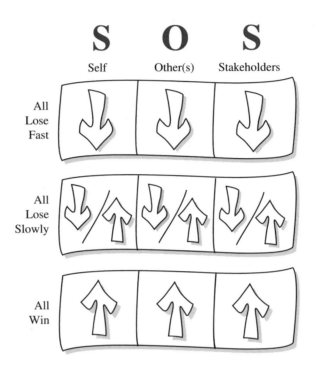

Consider these points about attitude:

Discounting someone in the SOS system usually results in a poor solution to an issue or decision that affects both you and the others.

Counting all parts of SOS, while sometimes difficult and complicated, is essential for creating best-fit solutions to your challenging issues.

BEHAVIOR AND ATTITUDE — SKILL AND CARING

Skilled or unskilled communication behaviors in combination with an uncaring or a caring attitude typically bring certain kinds of outcomes. They also influence personal esteem and relationship development.

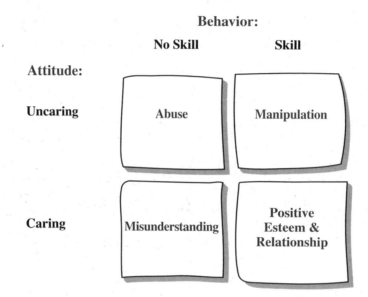

Behavior:

	No Skill	Skill
Attitude:		
Uncaring	Abuse	Manipulation
Caring	Misunderstanding	Positive Esteem & Relationship

- Lack of skill and an uncaring attitude — either toward self or another — produce abusive situations. These can extend from verbal or psychological abuse all the way to physical abuse.

- Skilled behavior with an uncaring attitude can permit you to manipulate or take advantage of another, particularly if the other is less skilled.

- Lack of skill, even with a caring attitude, can result in misunderstanding and unclear or inept communication.

- Skilled behavior and a caring attitude help you resolve issues effectively while you develop good self- and other-esteem in your exchanges; plus they help you strengthen your relationships.

Skills are Learnable

When you combine the communication skills with a caring attitude toward yourself, others, and stakeholders, you can work out the issues of your life more satisfactorily. Yet beyond that, the skills allow you to enjoy your relationships more. This workbook provides you with the means to learn and apply the skills and the processes that build upon those skills, as well as to discover their benefits in your connections with others.

 **Exercise**

DISCOUNTING OR COUNTING SOS

One way to understand an important issue/situation is to think about who is being counted or discounted.

Instructions

1. Think about a specific event, decision, or experience involving yourself and other(s) *that did not go well.* From your perspective, what happened? Describe the:

Situation	SOS Persons Counted/ Discounted	Behaviors	Outcome/Impact

2. Think about a specific event, decision, or experience involving yourself and other(s) *that went well.* From your perspective, what happened? Describe the:

Situation	SOS Persons Counted/ Discounted	Behaviors	Outcome/Impact

THE APPROACH IN THIS WORKBOOK

Core Communication offers you an integrated system of:

- Maps
- Skills
- Processes
- Guidelines

In addition to providing a practical knowledge base, these give you tools to build your interpersonal behavioral competence while incorporating an attitude of caring.

The text is organized into four sections:

- Communication Styles

    Chapter 1 lays out a map for understanding different ways — functions and impacts — that people talk to each other.

- Self-Awareness and Talking Skills

    Chapters 2 and 3 introduce you to types of issues, a map for understanding yourself and situations better, and six talking skills that give voice to your awareness.

- Other-Awareness and Listening Skills

    Chapter 4 sensitizes you to nonverbal communication of others, and Chapter 5 provides a map of five effective listening skills.

- Interactional Processes and Guidelines

    Chapter 6 describes processes in conflict, and Chapters 7 and 8 put the skills together with guidelines for you to stay skilled, even in challenging situations. Chapters 9 and 10 provide additional practical applications for making decisions, resolving conflicts, and planning important conversations.

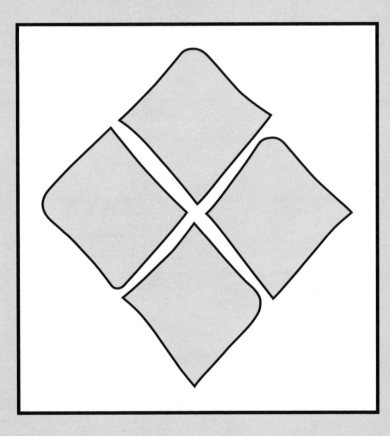

1

THE COMMUNICATION STYLES MAP

Styles of Talking
Your Brain and Styles
The "Low Road" and the "High Road"

When you talk with someone, each time you say something, your message contains two parts:

- *What* you say — the content
- *How* you say it — the style

What you talk about makes a difference, yet your style — *how* you talk about something — has the greatest impact on your communication. Your verbal and nonverbal style is a command or relational message. It tells others the way to take your message about the content — shows whether you are joking, angry, tentative, or serious. *Style also conveys a caring or uncaring attitude.*

Likewise, you display a style of listening, which can vary from one situation to the next. *How* you listen has a measurable effect on the quality of information the other person shares.

Since people respond to *how* as much as they do to *what,* the outcome of a conversation can change considerably depending on the talking and listening styles you use in the process. Your style either helps or interferes with your ability to connect and communicate effectively.

Many "failures to communicate" stem from using an ineffective style of communication for the situation.

COMMUNICATION STYLES MAP

How you talk and listen to someone falls into one of four major communication styles, shown in the map below:

- Each of the talking styles corresponds to a listening style.
- Every style has typical behaviors — unskilled or skilled — associated with it that have a highly predictable impact upon a conversation.

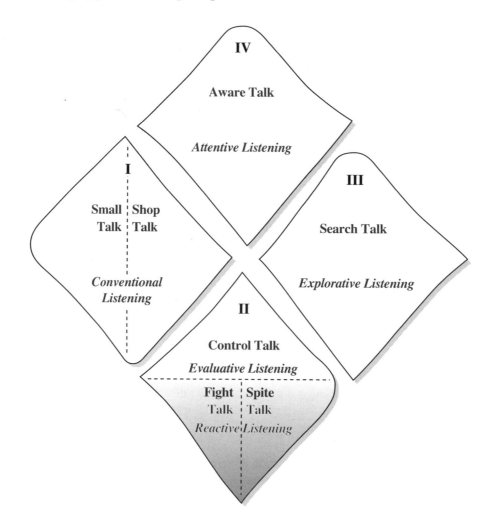

This chapter focuses on talking, the sending side of a conversation. Chapter 5 presents styles of listening, the receiving side of communication.

STYLES OF TALKING

STYLE I — Small Talk and Shop Talk

Small Talk and Shop Talk are the pleasant ways people use to connect and to exchange routine information.

SMALL TALK

Small Talk is the light conversation or chit chat about everyday things. It ranges from being cordial with strangers to enjoying time with friends or family. While this way of talking may be commonplace, it is very important for building rapport or relaxing with others.

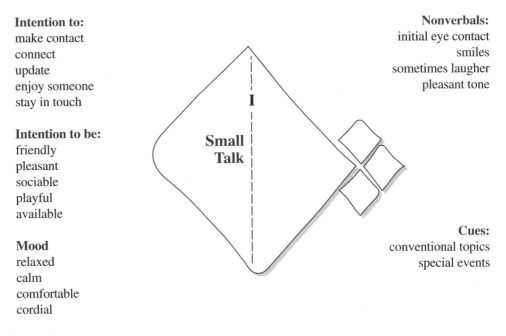

Intention to:
make contact
connect
update
enjoy someone
stay in touch

Intention to be:
friendly
pleasant
sociable
playful
available

Mood
relaxed
calm
comfortable
cordial

Nonverbals:
initial eye contact
smiles
sometimes laugher
pleasant tone

Cues:
conventional topics
special events

I

Small Talk

This style:

- Facilitates comfortable "comings" and "goings," connecting and disconnecting.
- Provides a way of simply being with someone or sharing activities in a relaxed manner.
- Reduces stress with a good joke or story and a laugh together.
- Diminishes in a hurried or pressured atmosphere, and evaporates with extended tension or conflict.
- Can be used to cover, skirt, deflect, or avoid dealing with an unresolved issue.

Typical Small-Talk Behaviors

Greetings, hellos and goodbyes: "Hi, how's it going?" "See you later."

Commenting on news, weather, sports: "Do you think it will rain tomorrow?" "I heard one of our players is on the injury list this week."

Sharing experiences and events of the day: "My biology professor didn't show up today, so I had more time to study for the calculus exam tomorrow . . ."

Lighthearted, non-hostile joking: "You're not a very good influence on me."

Storytelling: "When I was growing up, my Dad would say . . . ."

Discussing biographical data, general habits, or health "Where did you live when you were a child? . . . " "I seldom miss breakfast." "My elbow has been sore lately."

Impact of Small Talk

- Relaxes or refreshes a time together.
- Sometimes lightens a tense mood and eases pressure.
- Keeps conversation on an ordinary, surface level.
- Fosters annoyance if the other person wants to go to a more serious or deeper level.

Small Talk connects people.
Without it, you grow or stay distant.

SHOP TALK

Shop Talk is the conversation about tasks and necessary information to get a job done.

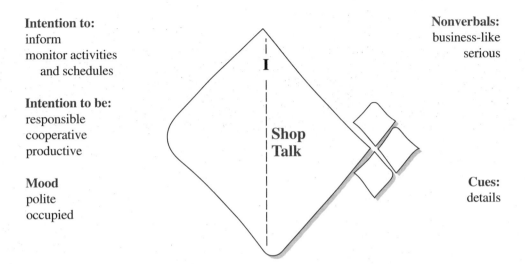

Intention to:
inform
monitor activities
and schedules

Intention to be:
responsible
cooperative
productive

Mood
polite
occupied

Nonverbals:
business-like
serious

Cues:
details

I

**Shop
Talk**

Typical Shop Talk Behaviors

Planning, scheduling: "How about meeting tomorrow afternoon?"

Reporting facts, observations: "I haven't seen any postings about who is on that study group."

Taking initiative, checking up, following up: "Did any of those numbers come in yet?"

Coordinating, making routine decisions: "I plan to leave early on Friday, as long as Joe has agreed to cover any walk-ins."

Impact of Shop Talk

- Handles routines or informs of changes in the maintenance of a system.

> Shop Talk keeps things moving, organized, and task oriented, but if that is all there is for you with others, you share little closeness.

Pause: Take a minute to reflect on when and with whom you use Small Talk and Shop Talk.

STYLE II — Control, Fight, and Spite Talk

Through power and control, this style aims at gaining agreement or compliance, or it attempts to resist change. When using Style II, you strive for a certain outcome, even if it has to be forced. You focus on the other person — not yourself.

People try to exert their power using three different ways of talking in Style II. The first way — Control Talk — sends messages intended to be constructive. The other two — Fight Talk and Spite Talk — send negative, potentially destructive messages. Nonverbals — posture, gestures, tone, pitch, pace and facial expressions— play a prominent role in signaling these messages.

CONTROL TALK

Control Talk intends to take charge — communicating a knowing, authoritative stance. This is a style most people use to direct, command, make a presentation, persuade, bargain, supervise, teach, and advocate.

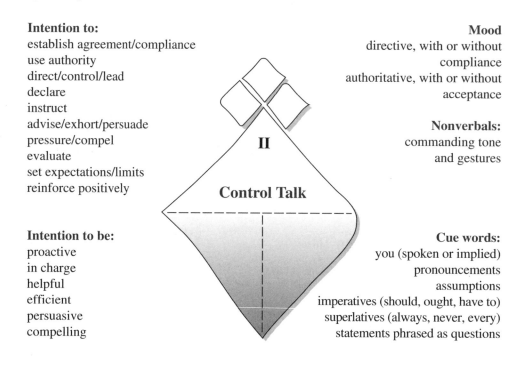

Intention to:
establish agreement/compliance
use authority
direct/control/lead
declare
instruct
advise/exhort/persuade
pressure/compel
evaluate
set expectations/limits
reinforce positively

Intention to be:
proactive
in charge
helpful
efficient
persuasive
compelling

Mood
directive, with or without compliance
authoritative, with or without acceptance

Nonverbals:
commanding tone and gestures

Cue words:
you (spoken or implied)
pronouncements
assumptions
imperatives (should, ought, have to)
superlatives (always, never, every)
statements phrased as questions

II

Control Talk

Typical Control-Talk Behaviors

Speaking for others — tell others what their experience has been, is, or will be: "You know this is the right decision."

Directing: "Turn it in by 12 noon sharp."

Advising, prescribing solutions: "Take some vitamin C. It will help you ward off a cold."

Advocating, persuading: "Just try it once. You will really like it."

Instructing: "There are three things to consider. The first is . . . ."

Evaluating: "This new software is twice as good as the old program."

Assuming: "It isn't hard. You can figure it out."

Setting expectations, establishing boundaries: "Let's get together tomorrow afternoon, just the two of us."

Cautioning, warning: "Be careful. The roads are slick."

Closed/directive questions: "Don't you think that . . . ?" "Wouldn't you agree that . . . ?

Praising: "You look great in your new hair style."

Bragging: "I'm always the one they count on."

Impact of Control Talk

- Shows the situation is under control, when it works.

- Fosters resistance if it is experienced as "boxing in" the other. (Most people like to participate in conversations and decisions that affect them; few like to be ordered around.)

- Sometimes creates misunderstanding and distance or an atmosphere of tension and pressure in its commanding tone.

- Can generate a Fight-Talk or Spite-Talk response, if it is taken as abrasive or discounting.

> If Control Talk goes on constantly between you and another person,
> you are caught in a power struggle with each other.

FIGHT TALK

Fight Talk strives to force change by intimidating others and defending self. It is an active, one-up, aggressive style — attempting power-over-other(s).

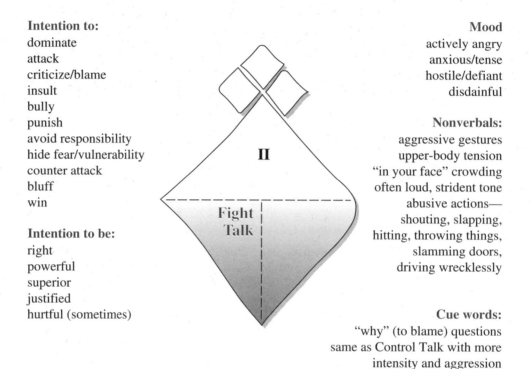

Intention to:
dominate
attack
criticize/blame
insult
bully
punish
avoid responsibility
hide fear/vulnerability
counter attack
bluff
win

Intention to be:
right
powerful
superior
justified
hurtful (sometimes)

Mood
actively angry
anxious/tense
hostile/defiant
disdainful

Nonverbals:
aggressive gestures
upper-body tension
"in your face" crowding
often loud, strident tone
abusive actions—
shouting, slapping,
hitting, throwing things,
slamming doors,
driving wrecklessly

Cue words:
"why" (to blame) questions
same as Control Talk with more
intensity and aggression
profanity and foul language

This talking style:

- Erupts around blocked desires or broken expectations.

- Covers emotions of disappointment, frustration, anxiety or fear.

- Focuses on persons rather than the issue.

- Discounts, devalues others.

- Ventilates, "acts out" anger.

- Is out of touch with self and other-awareness, consequently is out of control.

Typical Fight Talk Behaviors

Criticizing: "You never think before you act."

Defending: "I did it the right way, whether you think so or not."

Blaming, accusing, attacking, scolding: "It's your fault. You weren't paying attention."

Threatening, Intimidating: "I'll be watching every move you make."

Demanding, ordering: "Do it the way I say, or don't do it at all."

Arguing: "That's not right. It doesn't work that way."

Putting down, belittling, insulting, ridiculing: "If you had a brain in your head, you wouldn't know what to do with it."

Attributing, projecting: "You messed up again. You'll never learn."

Pronouncing ultimatums: "Do that one more time and you've had it!"

Labeling, stereotyping: "You're lazy and irresponsible."

Name-calling: "Hey stupid, how many times do I have to tell you? That's not the way to do it!"

Bullying, challenging, taunting: "You can't take it! Come on, take a swing at me."

Impact of Fight Talk

- Gets juices flowing and may break up a logjam once in awhile.
- Breeds defensiveness, resistance, tension and stress in others.
- Fuels arguments that can escalate to physical violence and abuse, creating an unsafe environment.
- Leaves others angry, wanting to get even.
- Ironically, gives away (loses) personal power.
- Often damages relationships by saying and doing mean and hurtful things that are later regretted.
- Blocks vital information and collaborative solutions to challenging issues.

Fight Talk signals one or more unresolved issue(s).

SPITE TALK

Spite Talk is an indirect attempt to bring down someone or something. It is a passive, one-down, aggressive style — exerting power-under-other(s).

People resort to spiteful messages when they believe they have no other way to influence others, or they have a hidden agenda.

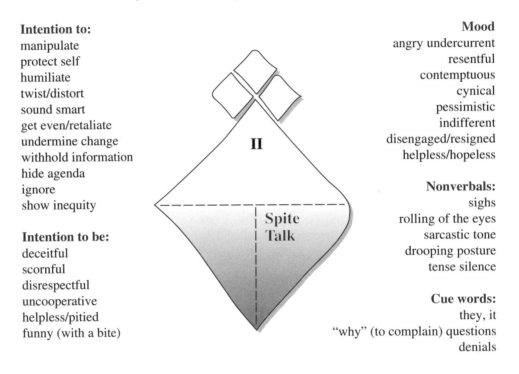

Intention to:
manipulate
protect self
humiliate
twist/distort
sound smart
get even/retaliate
undermine change
withhold information
hide agenda
ignore
show inequity

Intention to be:
deceitful
scornful
disrespectful
uncooperative
helpless/pitied
funny (with a bite)

Mood
angry undercurrent
resentful
contemptuous
cynical
pessimistic
indifferent
disengaged/resigned
helpless/hopeless

Nonverbals:
sighs
rolling of the eyes
sarcastic tone
drooping posture
tense silence

Cue words:
they, it
"why" (to complain) questions
denials

This talking style:

- Is indirect and angry, often covering underlying hurt, distrust, or resentment.

- Exercises power as powerlessness — uses disengagement, passivity, non-compliance, sabotage, or retaliation to manipulate.

- Exerts control from "weakness," rather than from a position of strength.

- Discounts, devalues self, communicating a "poor-me" attitude.

- Often complicates issues by complaining inappropriately to a third person.

- Sees self as a "victim" rather than an "agent" who makes things happen.

- Can represent either a long-term personal lifestyle of low self-esteem, or a temporary, wounded response to a particular situation.

Typical Spite-Talk Behaviors

Shooting zingers, taking cheap shots: "If you're so smart, you do it."

Cynicism, sarcasm, disgust: "Look who claims to have all the answers."

Complaining, whining, implying "poor me, ain't it awful": "How come I always have to do the dirty work?"

Pouting, withdrawing angrily, withholding affection: (going about business in silent unresponsiveness)

Making excuses: "Everybody else does it, too."

Stonewalling, refusing to answer when questioned

Withholding information: "If you didn't hear me the first time, I' not going to repeat it."

Denying, : "No, nothing's wrong. What makes you think that?"

Lying, distorting, misleading: "I called Jason yesterday (no call was made)."

Keeping score/reprisals: "I won't forget what you just said."

Giving in grudgingly, placating: "No, that's all right. Let's do it your way. I'm sure it will come out better than if we do what I want."

Being a martyr (covering for others, accepting blame): "It was probably my fault again. I should have . . . ."

Putting self down: "If I wasn't so dumb, I would have caught the mistake."

Attempt to humiliate, guilt, shame other: "I can't believe you did that."

Gossiping/being self-righteous: "I would never think of stooping that low."

Mean teasing: Mocking and poking fun at someone when that person does not think it is funny.

Impact of Spite Talk

- Seeds and feeds conflict "under the table."
- Drains, diffuses energy and stifles creativity.
- Thwarts change and brings discouragement to anyone involved.

> Spite Talk signals one or more unresolved issue(s).

Both Fight Talk and Spite Talk:

- Broadcast anger.
- Impact health negatively.
- Maintain self-deception, if continued.
- Disregard self's contribution and response to the situation.
- Yield win/lose, or both-lose outcomes.

These styles attempt to command and control through destructive behavior or defend against the same type of actions by others.

Pause: Take a minute to reflect on when and with whom you use Control, Fight, or Spite Talk.

STYLE III — Search Talk

Search Talk is an open and rational way of talking. It examines facts, suggests options, and gains an overview — to see the big picture.

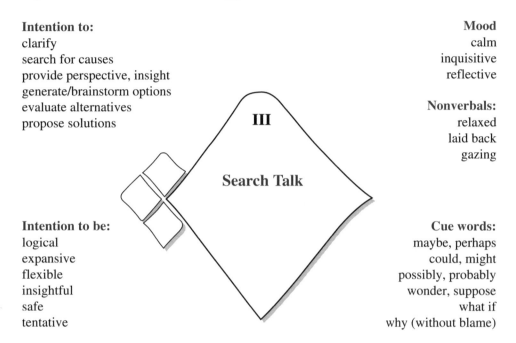

Intention to:
clarify
search for causes
provide perspective, insight
generate/brainstorm options
evaluate alternatives
propose solutions

Intention to be:
logical
expansive
flexible
insightful
safe
tentative

Mood
calm
inquisitive
reflective

Nonverbals:
relaxed
laid back
gazing

Cue words:
maybe, perhaps
could, might
possibly, probably
wonder, suppose
what if
why (without blame)

This talking style:

- Provides a safe way to approach an issue that is non-routine, complex, or uncertain.

- Offers a good way to shift away from an argument (Style II), to reduce pressure, and to expand information.

- Focuses more on past or future time-frames than on the experience of the present.

- Lacks, by itself, commitment to future action.

Typical Search-Talk Behaviors

Identifying issues: "I'm wondering if I'm studying so much I've let exercising and healthy eating go."

Giving relevant background information: "Last year the tests showed. . ."

Analyzing, considering causes: "Maybe because things came so easy for me so long, I got overconfident."

Giving opinions, impressions, explanations: "I think I eat too much fast food."

Making interpretations, speculating: "That phone message probably means they're still interested in talking."

Brainstorming, generating possibilities: "Perhaps I could check into graduate programs in the metro area, or maybe I could explore online options."

Making suggestions: "I suggest I think about it for a week or so."

Play out various scenarios without committing to any particular action: "If I got up fifteen minutes earlier in the morning, I could beat the traffic, or, if I took the toll-road, I could make better time."

Posing solutions: "One of us could try this for a month and then make a final decision."

Impact of Search Talk

- Gets new ideas into the open.

- Becomes a "think-tank" to play out or expand options for the future.

- Is a safe way to "test the water" with observations or possibilities.

- Risks skimming across the surface and missing important underlying emotional aspects of an issue.

- Can be a way to avoid resolving an issue, if no one takes responsibility for putting ideas into action.

> Search Talk shows willingness to approach and explore issues.

Pause: Take a minute to reflect on when and with whom you use Search Talk.

STYLE IV — Aware Talk

Aware Talk discloses all parts of a person's experience regarding a situation. This style reveals information left unsaid in other styles — typically emotions, wants, and commitments to act. It draws on power from within and shares that power with other(s).

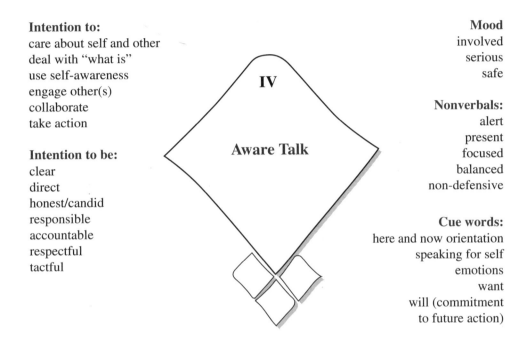

Intention to:
care about self and other
deal with "what is"
use self-awareness
engage other(s)
collaborate
take action

Intention to be:
clear
direct
honest/candid
responsible
accountable
respectful
tactful

Mood
involved
serious
safe

Nonverbals:
alert
present
focused
balanced
non-defensive

Cue words:
here and now orientation
speaking for self
emotions
want
will (commitment
to future action)

In Aware Talk, you go to the heart of an issue by:

- *Focusing* on your own experience in the present, now.
- *Accepting* what you find as *what is*, rather than disregarding, denying, or running from it.
- *Owning* your own *contributions* and *responses* to an issue or situation.
- *Disclosing* your awareness honestly and skillfully.
- *Resolving* matters constructively.

In this talking style, you:

- Use your emotions congruently.
- Deal productively with tension, differences, and conflict — without blaming, defending, or deceiving (Style II behaviors).
- Seek collaboration.

- Channel your energy into positive action.
- Manage self, rather than manipulate others.

Aware Talk:

- Is assertive and caring without being aggressive or defensive.
- Approaches with a softer tone, displaying a willingness to cooperate, rather than a harder, more callused one.
- Enables you to discuss a difficult matter effectively if your intentions are to connect and collaborate rather than to command and control.

Typical Aware Talk Behaviors

Speaking for self — not the other person.

Speaking about self, owning and sharing your own experience (using the Awareness Wheel and the six Talking Skills presented in chapter 3).

Dealing with the issue: "Here's how I see what's going on."

Acknowledging differences: "My impression is that we are at opposite poles on this point."

Recognizing tension: "I'm feeling frustrated right now."

Revealing impact: "When you said that, I felt sad."

Taking responsibility for your own contribution/response: "I didn't really listen to you. I assumed that I knew what you felt, so I started thinking about what to do next instead of listening."

Giving support, disclosing wants for another: "I've heard you say you want to visit your family. I'd like for you to have that happen."

Making an offer: "I'm willing to come in some evening or on the weekend, if that would help."

Committing to action, making and fulfilling promises: "Since that bothers you, I won't say it again."

Sharing hopes, dreams, plans: "I'd like to go back to school to prepare for a career shift."

Giving encouraging feedback: "I thought you did a great job of standing up respectfully against her pressure. To me that showed strength!"

Requesting feedback: "Have you noticed, after I ask Matt for his ideas, whether I do something that prevents him from giving them?"

Disclosing vulnerability, weakness: "Basically, I don't feel as confident as I let on."

Repairing, apologizing, asking for forgiveness: "I think I offended you by not getting your input. I'm sorry I did that. I want to apologize and assure you that I will not do that again."

Asking for change: "The joke about my socks isn't funny for me anymore. I don't want to hear it again. Will you agree to stop saying it?"

Expressing appreciation: "Thank you for your encouragement. Your support gives me confidence to move ahead on this tough decision."

Impact of Aware Talk

- Results in more helpful information and richer interchange.
- Builds trust as you share your real thoughts, emotions, and wants about issues.
- Demonstrates commitment to an open process, while bringing issues to closure.
- Can be transformational.
- Gets things done — is action oriented.

Aware Talk Brings Risk and Opportunity

- As you disclose more about yourself, you increase your listener's choices — what that person can do constructively or destructively about the information you supply.
- Usually disclosure begets disclosure and results in new understanding and satisfaction.

  With these principles about disclosure in mind, you can use judgment about the amount of self information you share with others regarding an issue.

> Using Aware Talk in a serious conversation enables you to discuss things of importance to you and others at a productive level.

Pause: Take a minute to reflect on when and with whom you use Aware Talk.

YOUR BRAIN & STYLES OF COMMUNICATION

The style of communication you use or choose at any point in time results from two forces: *instinct* and *learning*, both of which reside in your mind-brain. Three distinct but interconnected levels, with interrelated parts, form the whole of your brain. Each of these areas — action, emotional, and thinking subsystems — carries out a particular function.

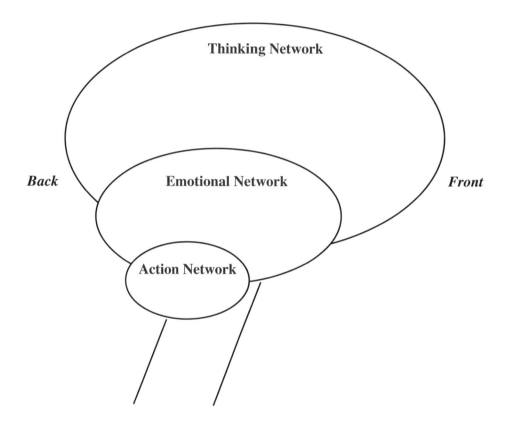

Your Action Network

The brainstem rests at the top of the spinal cord, at the base of the brain. The configuration is referred to as the "root brain." This area transfers action to the body. This network:

■ Cannot think or feel.

■ Is preset to regulate many basic bodily functions, such as respiration and metabolism, to ensure survival.

■ Implements behavior.

Your Emotional Network

The second level, middle area of the brain, houses emotional circuitry. It is comprised of what is often called the limbic system. This emotional center:

■ Generates our full range of emotions, including joy, happiness, sexual excitement, surprise and sadness, as well as feelings of fear, anxiety, and anger.

■ Reads another person's emotions through nonverbals.

■ Gives us capacity to connect or empathize with someone else's emotion.

■ Influences our ability to remember and learn.

■ Is always "on" — alert and constantly monitoring our physical and social environments.

■ Is primarily *reflexive*, ready to react to any sign of threat or danger.

Your Thinking Network

The third and highest level of the brain contains the thinking subsystem — the large area at the top of your brain — called the neocortex. This network:

■ Enables you to expand awareness, think abstractly and comprehend.

■ Gives the ability to access and analyze information, plan, and execute actions.

■ Can consider, regulate, and talk about the emotional networks's experience.

■ Is involved in the transmission of cultural knowledge and moral development.

■ Has the potential to operate collaboratively with conscious intent, a high order of social activity and relationship.

■ Is *reflective* in nature, allowing you to respond, rather than simply react.

THE "LOW ROAD" AND THE "HIGH ROAD

Neuroscientists speak of two general pathways for processing information in the brain. These can be referred to as two roads.

One pathway goes immediately through the circuitry of the emotional network, down to the root brain, to action. This route, called the *low road*, is:

- Reflexive and reactive.

- Largely unconscious and instinctual.

- Your "default system," ready for a fight or flight reaction.

- Very powerful and able to overwhelm and limit the executive functions of the thinking brain.

- Expressed in Fight Talk and Spite Talk — communicating the distressed, aggressive and defensive aspects of the emotional brain.

The other pathway activates the networks of the thinking area of the brain to process information and provide choices of behavior. This avenue, called the *high road*, is:

- Reflective and proactive.

- Consciously aware, creative and potentially collaborative.

- Capable of integrating and managing powerful drives and emotions originating in the middle brain subsystem.

- Active in Search and Aware Talk.

Note

- The low road is fast, communicating nonverbally. The high road is slower, generating words.

- More neural pathways run from the emotional brain to the thinking brain, than run from the thinking brain to the emotional brain. This is partly why emotions can be overwhelming and sometimes difficult to manage.

- The low road comes naturally. The high road does not. It requires learning.

> Taking the "high road" enables you to deal
> with life's challenges effectively.

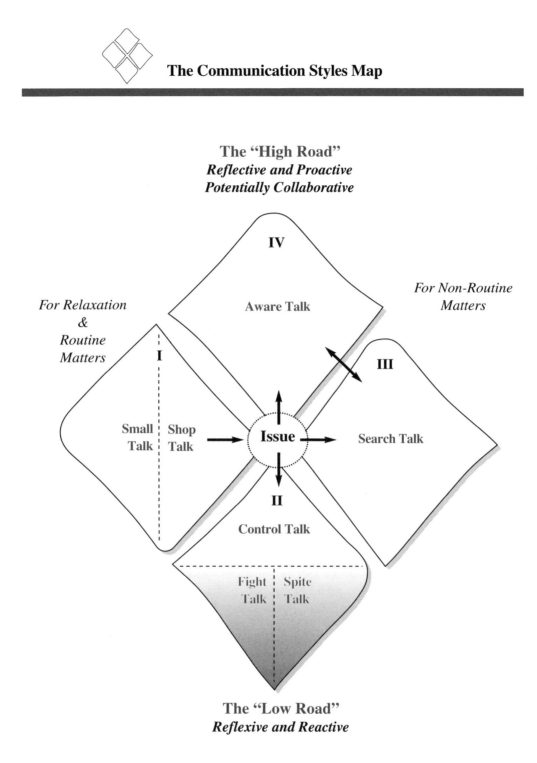

The "High Road"
Reflective and Proactive
Potentially Collaborative

IV

For Relaxation
&
Routine
Matters

Aware Talk

For Non-Routine
Matters

I

III

Small
Talk

Shop
Talk

Issue

Search Talk

II

Control Talk

Fight
Talk

Spite
Talk

The "Low Road"
Reflexive and Reactive

STYLES AND ROADS

When it comes to dealing with an issue, your style of communication reflects your mind-brain functioning — taking the "low road" or the "high road."

HANDLING LIFE'S CHALLENGES — the Road You Take

Style I

Hopefully you spend a good portion of your time in a calm, confident, and happy state reflected in your use of Small Talk. You can make your time productive with Shop Talk. Style I is generally used to relax, reconnect, or handle daily routines.

Style II — Takes the Low Road

However, from time to time an "alarm goes off" in your mind and body. The alarm system housed in the emotional network of your brain, signals caution, novelty, change, potential threat or even danger. This more or less anxious and uncertain state typically means a potential issue is at hand. (This is shown in the graphic on page 33 with an arrow pointing from Style I to "Issue" in the center of the graphic.)

The alarm can be set off by a comment from another person or from some other external source, as well as by a memory or an imagined event. Unless the alarm is so strong that it causes you to freeze or flee the situation (perhaps by returning inappropriately to Small Talk), the easiest and most efficient way to attempt to deal with the alarm is through Control Talk — taking charge and giving directives. (This is shown in the graphic by the arrow pointing from "Issue" to Style II.)

When it works (and others comply with your directives) the emotional center of your brain relaxes. You return to a calm and confident state.

Often however, in interactive situations, your Control Talk is by-passed or does not work, and you jump into Fight Talk to attack directly, or you slide indirectly into Spite Talk to "hit and run." When you go into Fight or Spite Talk, the emotional part of your brain has taken charge. It becomes more difficult to think clearly. Intentions of caring are pushed aside for control and self-protection.

If you allow your emotional brain to overwhelm you, often it requires a "time out" to calm and rebalance yourself. This gives the opportunity for you to reflect on the situation, and then you can shift to a more productive style of communication.

In interpersonal situations at home, school, work, or other places, Fight and Spite Talk reactions usually do not solve things. Instead, they typically make matters worse, escalate a conflict, and often result in relational damage and personal regret.

Style III — Starts the High Road

When a non-routine matter arises, rather than being driven by the raw emotion, it is possible to shift to thinking and talking about the issue using Search Talk. As you do so, you use your mind to reflect on the situation, speculate about what is going on, and possibly generate a solution. (This is shown in the graphic on page 33 with the arrow pointing from "Issue" to Style III.)

Search Talk is a safe way to initiate a conversation and to buy time to think about things, without necessarily taking action. In the process, you redirect your emotions from defensive action to cooperative action.

Style IV — Travels the High Road

To fully understand and resolve an issue, your thinking brain must incorporate and integrate important information from your emotional brain. The interactive process between the thinking part and the emotional part of your brain expands self-awareness (and other-awareness when someone else is involved). This action also builds relationship confidence, trust, and respect. (This is shown in the graphic by the arrowing pointing from "Issue" to Style IV.)

Aware Talk employs all of your conscious faculties to deal effectively with an issue/situation. It generates the richest information without attacking or defending anyone. Out of this, you can develop congruent, satisfactory, and action-oriented resolutions. You use your awareness to act constructively, to learn, and to grow. This road becomes the path to creating positive solutions.

Styles III and IV Together

Using a combination of Styles III and IV during a discussion about a *non-routine* matter is foundational to a productive conversation. (This is shown on the graphic by an arrow with two points going between Styles III and IV.)

CHOOSE HOW YOU COMMUNICATE

Understanding communication styles gives perspective about relating to others and about dealing with issues — effectively and ineffectively. This is particularly important to know when you are under pressure or when a conflict arises. You can learn how to communicate in constructive ways, taking the "high road" to meet the challenges of life.

After a chapter on issues, the rest of the workbook provides practical maps, skills, and processes — tools for activating the thinking part of your brain. These tools increase your choices for how you relate, so you can build satisfying connections and helpful solutions to the issues and situations that arise.

THE ROAD TAKEN

Instructions

Step 1. Recall a situation in which you were involved where people were using Small Talk or Shop Talk, and an issue arose, which caused someone to take the low road in communication. Reflect on whether anyone was able to bring people up to the higher road or whether others descended to the low road, too. If helpful, write notes below before going on to Step 2.

Situation:

Step 2. On the page across from here, draw arrows representing the path of the various people involved (jot down names on each arrow) until the situation ended. (See page 33 for the example diagram.)

3. Step 3. What was the result?

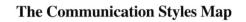
The "High Road"
Reflective and Proactive

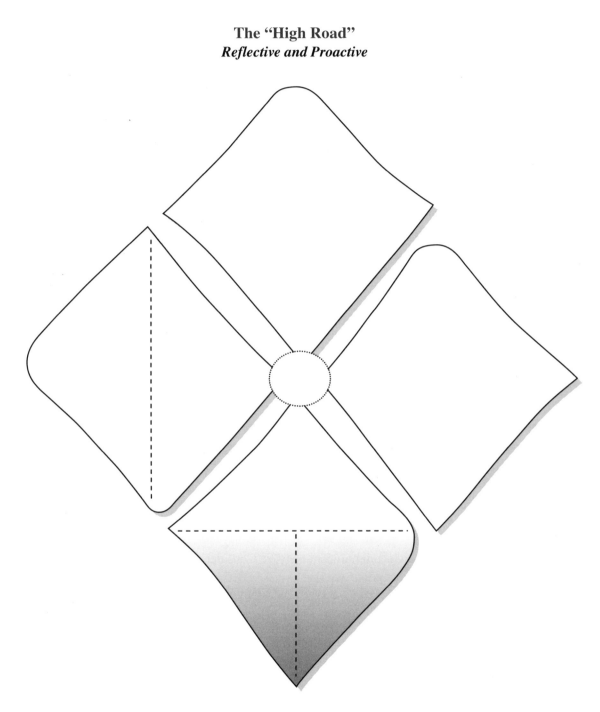

The "Low Road"
Reflexive and Reactive

MY TALKING STYLES

Instructions

Step 1. Think of the talking styles you use when you are conversing with people you relate to on a regular basis. Estimate the percentage of time you *typically* spend in each of the styles.

Typical   *Increase or Decrease*

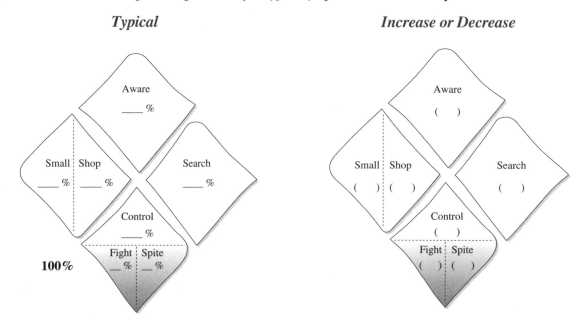

Step 2. Then, if you would like to change how you talk with these people, put a plus (+) in the style(s) you want to increase and a minus (-) in the ones you want to decrease.

Later . .

In the coming days, recognize your own communication styles. Consider various situations and how your use of styles either stays the same or changes.

Also, over the next few days, observe other people using various communication styles. In particular, listen for Fight or Spite Talk among friends or family, on news or opinion shows, or talk at work. Notice the impact these styles have on an interaction. Do you hear unresolved issues?

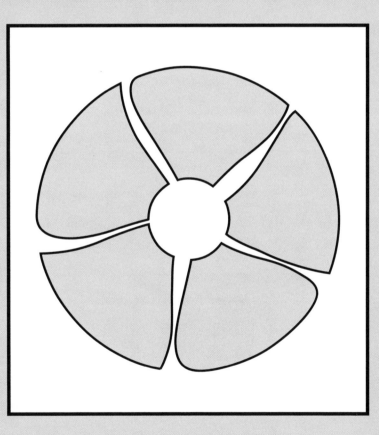

2

IDENTIFYING ISSUES

Types of Issues
The Third Force
Assumption in CORE

In the course of life, issues arise for everyone. These attention-getters emerge out of normal, daily situations and vary according to your stage in life. They crop up, for example, when you change jobs, go back to school, or move from one place to another — times when circumstances shift or opportunities appear. Issues erupt when something unexpected happens, including a crisis. They surface as you anticipate the future and make plans.

If an issue is present, your experiences relating to it and the details of it often become the focus of your conversation. It also can generate a conflict between you and another person. When you handle your concerns — whether small or large issues— effectively, you can prevent conflicts from developing between you and someone else, or you can resolve the conflicts that do occur more satisfactorily. Skills give you the means to accomplish these ends.

As you learn the communication skills in this program, you are encouraged to practice the skills on and apply them to your own issues. To give perspective (and provide guidance in selecting issues for practice), the following definition, framework, and examples may be helpful.

ISSUES — Life's Concerns and Opportunities

An issue is anything (behavior, event, information, situation, opportunity, or challenge) that concerns you or any other person in your SOS network. It usually involves making a decision.

Types of Issues

The issues you face, at one time or another, fall into four categories:

- Topical — about places, things, events, or tasks
- Personal — about yourself (or about other or stakeholder) as an individual in the SOS system
- Relational — between people (between yourself and other(s), or between other(s) and other(s), or between other(s) and stakeholder(s))
- Group — an organizational unit — family, work or leisure team, committee, or department

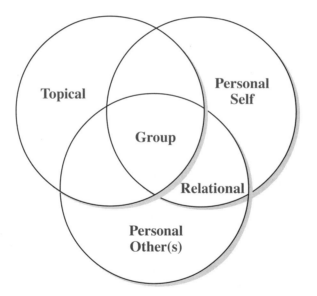

Knowing the differences among the types of issues can help you identify and deal with them more clearly and effectively.

TYPES OF ISSUES

Topical

Children	Friends	Pets
Chores	Family	Politics
Clothes	Housing	Projects
Drugs/Alcohol	Internet	Sports
Education	Money	Time
Exercise	Moving	Travel
Food	Parents	Work

Personal — Self *or* Other *or* Stakeholder

Appearance	Failure	Productivity
Attitude	Faith	Recognition
Career	Freedom	Responsibility
Creativity	Goals	Self-esteem
Death	Habits	Skills
Discipline	Health	Success
Energy	Identity	Values

Relational — Self *and* Other(s)

Closeness/Distance	Acceptance
Collaboration/Competition	Affection
Conflict/Harmony	Appreciation
Equality/Subordination	Boundaries
Inclusion/Exclusion	Commitment
Similarity/Difference	Communication
Stability/Change	Fun
Support/Control	Sex
Togetherness/Apartness	Trust

Group — as Unit

Esprit de corps
Feedback
Participation
Productivity
Purpose
Resources/Constraints
Stage of Development
Structure/Leadership

Consider These Points

- Issues tend to increase in importance and consequence as the focus moves from topical to relational.

- An issue may not always fit just a single category. Rather, it may be composed of a combination of types, which interrelate and impact each other. For instance, you want to earn or save money (topical) to go back to school in order to advance your career (personal); this desire could affect the togetherness or acceptance of the person with whom you live (relational).

- Issues require varying amounts of mental, emotional or physical energy (as well as of material resources) to resolve, depending on their significance.

- Any issue can become a conflict. When people in your SOS network have apparent differences — perceptions, interpretations, emotions, or interests regarding an issue — that are expressed in certain actions, conflict can emerge or erupt.

LIST OF MY CURRENT ISSUES

Date: _____

Instructions: Take a few minutes, relax, and think about what is going on in your life at the present time. Think about your activities at home, work, school, and elsewhere. As you reflect, write down a word or phrase that represents the topical, personal, or relational concerns that come to your mind. (If something is too personal for this setting, you may choose not to write it down.)

Issues

THE THIRD FORCE

In any conversation relating to an issue, three forces are at work:

- The *content* — what it is all about — your experience of it and the information related to it.

- The *outcome* — a satisfying solution being sought or the result from it.

- The *process* — how you talk and listen to one another (your communication style). Process is the way you deal with content and develop an outcome regarding an issue.

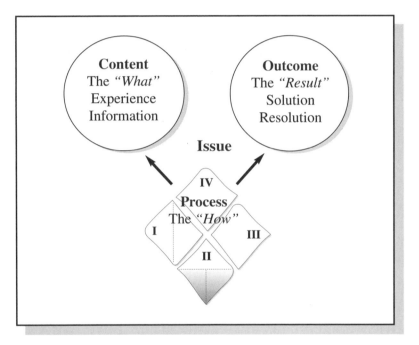

Conversations about issues typically focus on the content or the outcome, without attention to the process. While all three forces are important, the biggest influence on the quality of the content expressed and the outcome developed is the process used. It is a third force that supports or inhibits helpful discussion and satisfying resolution.

ASSUMPTION IN CORE

The concepts and skills in CORE COMMUNICATION assume the following:

AN 80/20 RULE: LOOK INSIDE FIRST

This means that about 80 per cent of the time, the important *content* for creating satisfying *outcomes* to the challenging issues you face resides inside yourself and the others involved.

This rule of thumb applies to resolving:

- Your own personal issues
- Conflicts between you and other(s)
- Disputes within a group that you facilitate

The 80/20 rule supports self-awareness and awareness of others involved in an issue — important elements of personal and interpersonal competence.

Many people operate in the reverse — from a 20/80 perspective. They look largely to information outside of themselves as they deal with issues and resolve their conflicts.

CORE COMMUNICATION aims to increase your attention to process and to equip you with practical communication skills. The material shows you how you can gain awareness of the critical information (content) inside yourself and others, as you make decisions, negotiate differences, and build satisfying agreements (outcomes) for the issues you encounter throughout life.

3

THE AWARENESS WHEEL MAP

Your Self Awareness
Self-Talk
6 Talking Skills

Awareness — understanding yourself and others accurately, especially in relation to issues and situations — is foundational to effective communication. Really knowing what is going on inside yourself helps you talk more clearly and figure out solutions more readily. This chapter gives you a tool to unlock and increase your self awareness.

The tool, called the Awareness Wheel, is actually a map of your experience of an issue or situation. The map helps you to reflect on and clarify, at any moment in time, how you are responding to the issue. The tool is particularly useful when a conflict arises. It allows you to travel the high road — to relate in ways that care for yourself and the other person(s) in the situation. The better you are at understanding yourself, the more effective and influential you can be in your interactions and relationships.

HOW YOU EXPERIENCE AN ISSUE

All issues — whether topical, personal, or relational — have an underlying, common structure. They are made up of five different types of information. Similar to the way a simple sentence contains basic parts — subject, verb, and object — your experience of an issue contains basic parts — your sensory data, thoughts, emotions, wants, and actions. The Awareness Wheel map presents the parts in an overall structure.

Each of the five parts — or zones —of the Awareness Wheel contains important information about yourself. The parts are:

- Distinct qualitatively.

- Connected, impacting one another.

- Present, whether or not you are conscious of them.

- Useful particularly when you tune into them.

Through its function as a map, the Awareness Wheel represents and integrates your whole brain — your root, emotional, and thinking brain areas. The following sections describe each of the zones of the Wheel and then explain how to use the map as a practical tool.

(Each person has his or her own Awareness Wheel, whether the person knows this or not. While this chapter helps you focus on understanding *your own* Wheel, Chapter 5 on listening will show you how to discover *someone else's* Wheel, too, which can be very useful during a conversation about an issue.)

> An important resource you bring to any situation is your ability to tune in to your own awareness.

PARTS OF THE AWARENESS WHEEL

SENSORY DATA — Inputs to You

Sensory Data are pieces of information you receive via your five senses: sight, hearing, smell, taste, and touch. They are what you perceive.

External Sources

You receive, through the five channels, non-verbal and verbal data about another person or other people. What you take in includes their:

actions	gestures	posture	silence
facial expressions	pitch/pace/tone	scent	words

Your brain also scans your environment constantly to pick up data from other sources, such as:

- Context — time, place — the surroundings.
- Electronic media and printed materials.

Internal Sources

Sensory data come to your awareness from inside your own body, as well. These include:

- Physical sensations — for example, the lack or presence of physical pain, muscle relaxation or tension, fatigue, hunger or fullness (satiation).
- Specific memories.
- Remembered dreams.
- Visualization, imagination — imagery of the future.

Functions of External and Internal Sources

Your five senses give you the ability to have:

- Immediate and historical (recalled) contact with your world.
- Details for describing (documenting) your observations.
- Imagined pictures (visualizations) of future possibilities.

The more observant you become to the details of your sensory data, the better you will become at using your own "database" effectively.

THOUGHTS — The Meaning You Make

Thoughts are the meanings you make out of the sensory data you receive.

The following four forms of thoughts correspond generally with your past, present, and future thinking:

- *Beliefs/assumptions* — what you hold to be true, useful, and valuable from your past experience that you bring to each new situation.

- *Interpretations* — the meaning or appraisal you make currently of sensory data. This includes logical and analytical processes of weighing data, as well as irrational (biased and distorted) thinking. Interpretations represent the way you put your world together at any point in time.

- *Expectations* — the future you anticipate or what you think will happen, based on what you have seen or heard — perceived — from some current or past sensory data. Expectations function as "future memories" — waiting to be fulfilled.

- *Possibilities* — the future you imagine — alternative ways of viewing the future.

Other words that signal thinking processes include:

assessments	constraints	impressions	potentials
assumptions	convictions	judgments	predictions
benefits	evaluations	metaphors	prejudices
biases	guesses	needs	principles
conclusions	hunches	opinions	reasons
consequences	ideas	objections	values

Points to Consider About Your Thoughts:

- Beliefs, interpretations, expectations, and possibilities are powerful forces. They are strong influences on your decisions and actions, and they can limit or expand what you do.

- Sometimes thoughts can be quite illogical or inconsistent with the evidence.

- It is possible to create (add), select (filter), or ignore (delete) pieces of sensory data to fit your beliefs, interpretations, and expectations. This results in bias and distortion.

- Thoughts often become self-fulfilling prophesies.

- Your self-esteem arises from your beliefs and judgments about yourself in various circumstances across time.

- Another person may see and hear the same data and come to very different conclusions.

- In addition to sensory data, other parts of the Awareness Wheel affect your thoughts.

EMOTIONS — Your Feelings

Emotions are your body's response to your interpretation of sensory data. Emotions are *alerted* by external or internal sensory inputs, which are quickly *appraised* to be safe or dangerous, pleasant or unpleasant. They *arouse* readiness to act — typically approach or withdrawal behavior.

Many of your emotions operate below the conscious level. They impact your chemistry, blood pressure, heart rate, and muscle tension and are observable by others as your non-verbal behaviors — facial expressions, bodily movements, or voice tone and intensity.

Upon reflection, emotions can be raised to consciousness where they can be considered, named, and managed. In many situations, you experience several different kinds of emotions at the same time.

Six Basic Emotions

Each of these six basic emotions is recognized non-verbally across cultures:

happiness   sadness   anger   fear   disgust   surprise

Other variations of emotions occur, as well. For example, you can feel:

amazed	delighted	frightened	peaceful
annoyed	disappointed	frustrated	pleased
anxious	discouraged	glad	proud
ashamed	eager	guilty	relieved
calm	elated	hurt	resentful
cautious	embarrassed	irritated	satisfied
comfortable	enthusiastic	jealous	scared
contented	excited	joyful	uneasy

Understanding Emotions

Emotions reflect what is happening in other parts of your Awareness Wheel. (They do not just come out of the blue.) For this reason, emotions are quite rational and predictable. This is why you can learn to trust your emotions as useable information.

For example, if what you hear (sensory data) matches or mismatches your expectations (thoughts), your corresponding emotions — from pleasing to disturbing — occur. If you hear that a particular job offer goes to someone else and you were expecting to receive that offer, you might feel disappointed, angry, and jealous. On the other hand, you might feel a little relieved, if part of you believes the job might be over your head or too demanding. The stronger your expectations, the stronger the resulting feelings.

Emotions have multi-functions:

- Like an alarm, they signal new or unresolved issues — that something is unsettling — originating in some zone of your Wheel.

- They are the internal indicators (feedback) of your level of satisfaction with the *process* (handling) and the *outcome* (result) of an issue.

Your body gives you clues to your emotions. If you tune into your body's internal sensations, you can often locate where you feel your emotions. For example, your:

- Stomach may give a certain sensation when you are excited or afraid.

- Upper body muscles tighten with distress or anger.

- Muscles relax with the feelings of happiness and peace.

Making Use of Emotions:

- Emotions regulate and direct the flow of energy through your body.

- Since emotions are part of *what is*, they do not have to be justified, denied, or avoided. If you do not attend to them, you miss important information that is essential for making good decisions or resolving conflicts.

- If your emotions are not distorted by drugs (sometimes including prescription drugs), alcohol, organic disease, or confused learning, your feelings function like an accurate gauge — a barometer. They give you a reliable reading of your situation.

- Emotions lend color to dry logic and cold facts.

- Even though your emotions occur outside your conscious control, once you gain awareness of them, you increase your ability to manage them. As you recognize and acknowledge them, you can learn ways to control yourself and express them appropriately.

Note a Common Confusion

Many people use the phrase, "I feel like" or "I feel that" and believe they are giving an emotion, however, they are really giving a thought. While using the word *feel* for *think* is common in our language, this use does not distinguish adequately your emotions from your thoughts. The two kinds of information are qualitatively distinct. Confusing the two limits the clarity of your awareness and the effectiveness of your communication.

Three examples of the confusion include:
　　"I feel like I'm *competent*."
　　"I feel that I'm *rejected.*"
　　"I feel *threatened.*"

These are really thoughts, which in these cases are evaluations of yourself or a situation. Notice what happens when you consider *competent*, *rejected* or *threatened* as thoughts, and not emotions: You recognize your thinking (your evaluations), and are aware of your associated emotions. For example:

　　"I believe I'm competent. I feel confident and pleased.

　　"I think I'm being rejected. I feel disappointed and discouraged."

　　"I suspect I'm being threatened. I'm scared and angry."

When an issue is involved, most thoughts have one or more emotions associated with them, or vice versa. Thoughts that typically produce considerable emotion are easy to confuse with feelings. For richer awareness and clearer communication, pay attention to the difference between your thoughts and your feelings.

Below is a partial list of some *thought words that are commonly expressed as emotions.* As you read over the list, identify the emotions (sometimes strong emotions) that often accompany these thoughts:

Betrayed	Dominated	Rejected
Challenged	Important	Respected
Cheated	Inadequate	Rewarded
Childish	Intimidated	Slighted
Competent	Incompetent	Tempted
Conspicuous	Insulted	Threatened
Deceitful	Persecuted	Thwarted
Defeated	Pressured	Unappreciated

WANTS — Your Desires

Wants are your wishes and intentions for yourself and for others, short-term or long-term, and general or specific.

Other common words associated with wants include:

aspirations	goals	inclinations	objectives
dreams	hopes	longings	targets
drives	intentions	motives	yearnings

Three types of wants, with examples, include:

- *To be*: healthy, honest, respected, appreciated, liked, successful.
- *To do* — general or specific

    General: compete, collaborate, get even, clarify, support

    Specific: finish a project, change jobs, go out for pizza

- *To have*: more time, a different car, good friends

Wants:

- Provide direction without commitment to action. They imply a movement towards or away from something or someone.
- Are what motivate and energize you. (Other people's wants are what motivate them.)
- Vary in intensity from weak to strong.
- Reflect your values.
- Sometimes start vaguely and then become more specific.
- Remain tentative, as intentions to act, until they are translated into future actions — next steps. By themselves, wants do not necessarily change things.

What You Want Comes Out Directly or Indirectly in Your Actions.

- You can have multiple wants, and they can either converge or compete with one another.

- When your wants are fragmented or conflicting, they scatter your energy and lead to incongruent behavior.

- Hidden wants (perhaps because they are not acceptable to yourself or others important to you) become hidden agenda. They result in confusing, misleading, or dishonest communication.

- Clarifying and prioritizing your wants can help focus your energy, increasing your effectiveness.

Wants *for* Versus *from*

When we attend to wants, we often first think of self: my interests, what I desire *for* myself. This demonstrates caring about self (which is important to recognize). When it comes to thinking about others, it is easy to think only about what I want *from* others (*for* self) — not *for* others (other persons or stakeholders), based on their interests.

S	**O**	**S**
Self	**Other(s)**	**Stakeholders**
Yourself	People who are *immediately/ centrally* involved	People who are *peripherally* involved yet still affected

Wants For Others and Stakeholders Build Bridges

Wants *for* other(s) means that I acknowledge others' interests — based on what I have heard them say they want. Wants *for* others involves, to the extent possible, wanting for them what they want for themselves, and supporting them in fulfilling their interests. This demonstrates caring about (counting) others.

The Big Test!

The big test is whether your wants for the others (in the SOS network) match *what they want for themselves* — based on *what they have actually indicated they want* (your sensory data). A match passes the test.

- Caution: It is easy to want *for* others what you think would be good for them (what they *should* want). This does not pass the test.

- Wants for others requires real understanding of another and the ability to put yourself in that person's shoes (discover his or her Awareness Wheel).

Motivation — Putting Wants to Work for You

- Everyone has wants and wants are motivators. If you want to motivate someone, discover and build on his or her interests.

- When you help others achieve their objectives, you strengthen relationships and typically gain support for your own interests.

- If you cannot affirm all of others' wants, at least acknowledge them and look for wants you can support. Usually, something exists around which you can connect and build.

- If you do not know what others want, ask them.

Wants Are a Critical Part of Solutions

- Wants *for* other(s) provide a potential connecting point — *the foundation for collaboration* — especially in negotiating, decision-making, and conflict-resolving situations.

- When you use your Awareness Wheel, you actively identify your wants *for* SOS — the whole system. This information supports the process of creating "best-fit" solutions, the most satisfying outcomes for everyone involved.

- Considering wants *for* SOS is critical for individual, pair, or group solutions.

- While not always easy, affirming wants for those in your SOS network is essential for effective systems thinking and change.

ACTIONS — Your Behavior

Actions are what you do and say — your nonverbal behavior and verbal statements — past, present, and future.

External Actions

Most actions are overt and observable, the resulting *output* of how you *process* your experience — sensory data, thoughts, emotions, and wants — consciously or unconsciously.

Internal Actions

Some actions occur internally and are typically less observable. Examples of internal actions include:

agreeing	disagreeing	reflecting	trusting
considering	doubting	listening	worrying

Owning Your Actions and the Time Factor

- Past Action: What you did or said earlier — yesterday, last week, last year, or before — *demonstrates accountability.*

- Current Action: What you do or say currently — *exhibits responsibility.*

- Expressing Future Action: what you will do at a specific point in time — an hour from now, tomorrow, or next week — puts will into motion and *proclaims commitment.*

Accountability — Responsibility — Commitment		
Past Action Did: → ←	**Current Action** Do: → ←	**Future Acton** Will do:
Accomplishments Achievements Activities Failures	Agreements/ Disagreements Recommendations Requests Suggestions	Announcements Declarations Plans Promises

Points to Consider

- Your Actions (output) become Sensory Data (input) for others.

- Expressing Future Actions involves commitment.

- Trust is built or destroyed through keeping or breaking commitments.

- People and organizations are known by the promises they keep. Take commitments to Future Action seriously.

- Committing to Future Action builds confidence, learning and growth.

Tips

- Future Actions are next steps.

- Wanting, intending to do something, and thinking about what you could do are not the same as committing to a Future Action.

- The key word for Future Action is "will." "I will do . . . , commit to . . . ."

- Big issues usually require small next steps. If you believe that big issues require big solutions, you may stay stuck. Small changes can leverage large changes in systems.

- Not every issue requires that you choose a Future Action immediately. You may need additional time to reflect.

- Not all issues require a Future Action. Sometimes understanding alone is the solution.

- Often failure to take a Future Action is simply avoidance of the issue.

EARLY WARNING SIGNALS TO ISSUES

A signal to an issue can come from any zone of your Awareness Wheel:

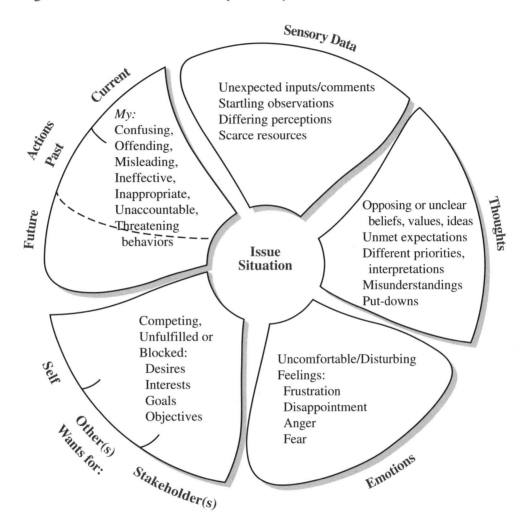

The Awareness Wheel can alert you to an issue, so you are able to reflect on it for ultimately resolving it. One way to do this occurs through your self-talk, as described in the following section.

SELF-TALK: PROCESSING AN ISSUE INTERNALLY

Self-talk is your internal conversation — the process of reflecting on all parts of your Awareness Wheel in order to understand, clarify, and resolve an issue/conflict.

Using the Awareness Wheel for Self-Talk

To use the Awareness Wheel as a tool for self-talk regarding an issue:

- Privately ask yourself, "What is going on right now? What am I experiencing?"

- Develop and organize your awareness to analyze the issue.

- Cover all parts of the Wheel in any order — all parts of your Wheel are interrelated.

- Be honest with yourself. Accept what you find as where you are — the starting point for dealing with the issue.

- Fill in any blind spots (missing information).

- Decide if this is a topical, personal, relational, or a group issue or conflict.

- Note that you can experience the negative form of the zones of the Wheel: "I did not see . . . "; "I don't think . . . "; "I'm not happy . . . "; "I do not want . . . "; "I did not do . . . ."

Often by expanding and clarifying your awareness of the issue, something shifts internally, bringing all parts together, enabling you to choose a constructive next step (future action). A future action can be a small next step.

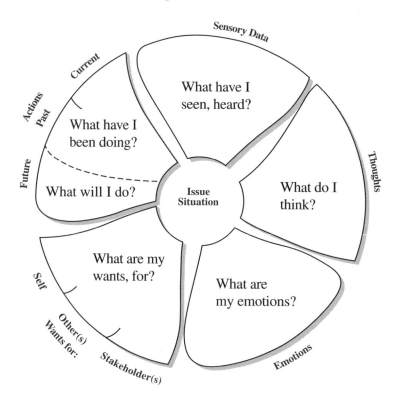

SELF-TALK

Instructions

Choose an issue — topical, personal, or relational — that you would be willing to share with two or three other people in a small group. (Refer to your list of issues in Chapter 2, page 44.)

Write the issue in the hub of the Awareness Wheel below. Then, fill out your Wheel, in any order, using key words or phrases that represent your experience regarding the issue.

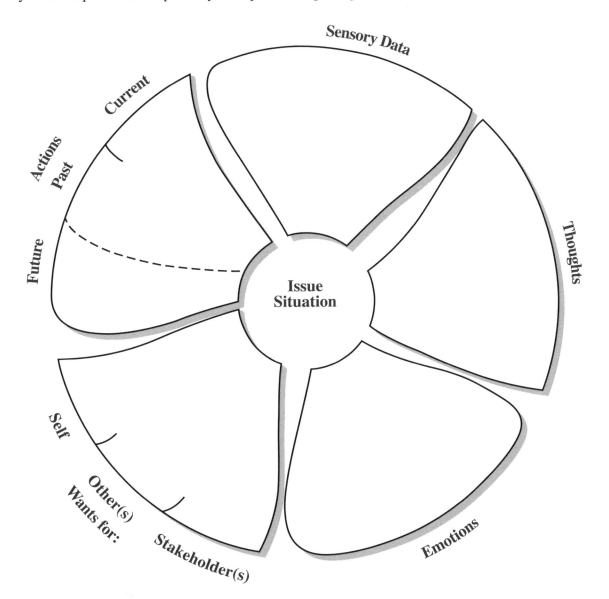

REAPPRAISING AN ISSUE/CONFLICT

If you find yourself stuck (unable to take a future action) or frustrated (experiencing an unsettling emotion) after initial work with the Wheel, you may want to try again. Sometimes it takes longer and another visit to reflect on the issue – depending on its complexity and importance — before it fits together.

By consciously reappraising a situation and reconsidering your data, thoughts, wants and actions – four parts of your Awareness Wheel – from a different perspective, you will often discover that new, clearer awareness emerges. As significant change occurs, your emotions will reflect this new state of affairs.

Remember the 80/20 rule: The most important information regarding an issue is inside yourself. Check inside first.

Tips for Reappraising an Issue

- Begin your reappraisal by taking a deep breath, letting yourself relax. This sends oxygen to your brain and allows deeper, less obvious (non-conscious) thoughts, emotions, and wants to surface. Like peeling an onion, you may discover other layers of your experience.

- While you can start your reappraisal in any part of the Wheel, it is often effective to consider the thinking portion first. When you do this, ask yourself, "Are there any other ways of interpreting the sensory data that I have? Can I look at the data without attributing a negative intent to someone else involved? What could be advantages to this situation?

- Sometimes the issue/conflict you start with is not the real issue/conflict. Rather, in the process of expanding your awareness, you discover a deeper, more central or encompassing concern to be the major issue. Begin a new Wheel, putting this more central issue in the hub.

- If a clear next step or new awareness does not emerge after recycling (reappraising) the Wheel a couple of times, set the issue (your Wheel) aside for a while. Go on living, letting your current awareness interact ("cook") with new data and emerging experience. In the meantime, you can be confident that you have a tool to help you manage yourself and the issue/conflict as it unfolds.

- Realize that in some instances, you must involve another person too, such as a coach, facilitator, or counselor to resolve an issue. By reappraising, using self-talk with the Wheel, you heighten your awareness of your choices, including a difficult one. You have a solid foundation for finding a solution.

WAYS TO REAPPRAISE THE ISSUE

Solutions to issues often reside in one or more zones of the Awareness Wheel. The challenge is to find the part or combination of parts inside yourself that leads to a constructive next step.

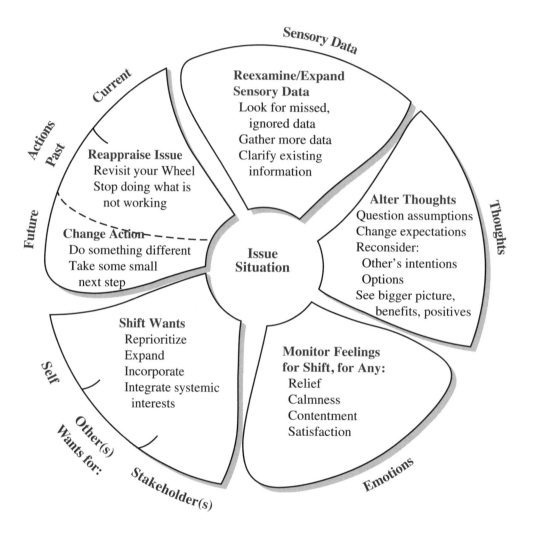

REAPPRAISAL EXERCISE

Instructions

If an obvious, constructive next step (Future Action) did not readily emerge from your self-talk on page 63, use the Wheel on this page to "reappraise" the issue/conflict. Offer yourself a second opinion.

Begin by taking a deep breath. Then as you go around your Wheel again, see if you can experience any or all of the parts differently. Use the suggested "Ways to Reappraise the Issue" on the previous page to assist your reappraisal.

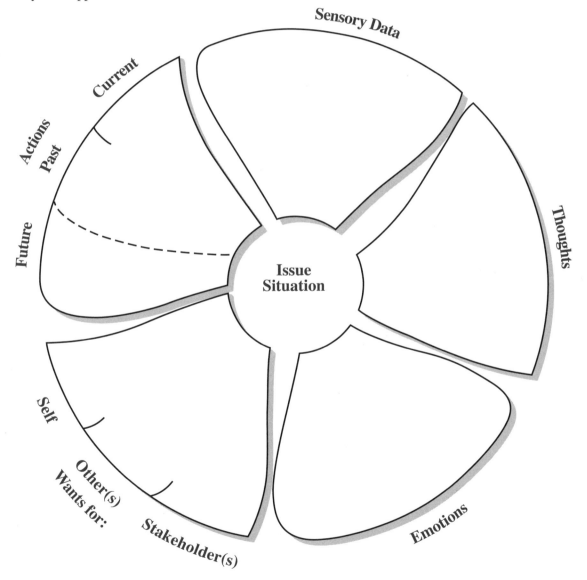

SIX TALKING SKILLS — for Aware Talk, Style IV

If you choose to share your self-information with someone else, six talking skills, based on the Awareness Wheel, will help you do so more clearly, directly, and completely. They give voice to your experience. The six skills are:

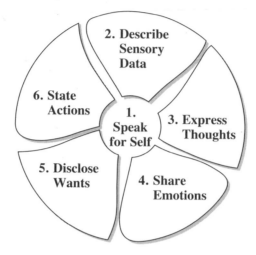

1. SPEAK FOR SELF

This skill is basic to all the other talking skills. It is critical to making your message more apt to be listened to and accepted rather than ignored and rejected.

To speak for yourself, combine a personal pronoun — I, me, or my — with any part(s) of your Awareness Wheel to form a message.

> "I saw you hesitate and then speak."
>
> "Here's my idea."
>
> "Your response really pleases me."
>
> "I'd like more time to think about it."
>
> "I will call you Thursday."

Benefits of Speaking for Self:

- Makes messages clearer and easier to hear
- Reduces defensiveness/resistance in others
- Allows and encourages other views — differences
- Values self, respects others

UNPRODUCTIVE ALTERNATIVES TO SPEAKING FOR SELF

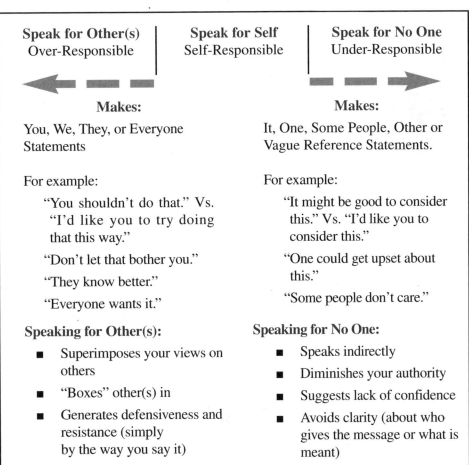

Speak for Other(s) Over-Responsible	Speak for Self Self-Responsible	Speak for No One Under-Responsible
←		→

Makes:

You, We, They, or Everyone Statements

For example:

"You shouldn't do that." Vs. "I'd like you to try doing that this way."

"Don't let that bother you."

"They know better."

"Everyone wants it."

Speaking for Other(s):

- Superimposes your views on others
- "Boxes" other(s) in
- Generates defensiveness and resistance (simply by the way you say it)
- Is often invasive, intrusive
- Denies difference, uniqueness
- Discounts others

Makes:

It, One, Some People, Other or Vague Reference Statements.

For example:

"It might be good to consider this." Vs. "I'd like you to consider this."

"One could get upset about this."

"Some people don't care."

Speaking for No One:

- Speaks indirectly
- Diminishes your authority
- Suggests lack of confidence
- Avoids clarity (about who gives the message or what is meant)
- Is cautious, uncommitted
- Seems distant, often formal
- Devalues self

Speaking for Self Counts Self by Demonstrating:

- Uniqueness — my individuality and diversity
- Ownership — my responsibility and accountability
- Confidence— the legitimacy and validity of my perspective
- Authority — my acknowledgement and acceptance of my experience
- Assertion — my right to speak my own awareness

2. DESCRIBE SENSORY DATA

Describe what you see, hear, touch, taste, or smell — your observations (verbal and nonverbal):

- Supply specific who, what, where, when, and how information. Give concrete examples.

  "This morning, I heard Jack say he has a ballgame this weekend."

- Include pertinent facts, figures, and information from print, electronic, or other sources.

  "I noticed the balance in my checking account has dropped below the required minimum."

- The more descriptive, specific, and pertinent the information is, the stronger the data.

3. EXPRESS THOUGHTS

Say what you think — believe, interpret, expect, imagine to be possible.

  "I think I can find a place to live that will be closer to work for me."

  "I believe that road will be closed for repairs."

Document

- Link interpretations to sensory data (observations). This lets others know how you have drawn your conclusions.

  "With only two days left, I don't think we are going to be ready to present the report."

  "I think my comment upset you. I noticed you got quiet."

4. SHARE EMOTIONS

Give your emotions directly.

- You can do so without using the word "feel." Simply say:

  "I'm thrilled about your promotion."

  "Waiting is frustrating for me."

  "I'm scared that I may have missed the deadline."

- Avoid using the common phrase, "I feel that . . . " This usually refers to a thought and does not clearly report an emotion.

- Directly identifying and giving words to emotions will help you:

  - Ground and discharge negative emotions effectively, freeing you to move on.

  - Add clarity to your communication.

5. DISCLOSE WANTS

*Directly express your desires for Self, Other(s), and **Stakeholders**.*

> "I'd like to make a decision as soon as possible, for my own scheduling."

> "I don't want you to be pressured to decide too fast. I heard you say you need some time to think about it" (sensory data).

> "I want the rest of the people in the building to find the decision satisfactory to them, too."

Note: Be sure to distinguish between wants *from* **O**ther or **S**takeholder (for you) and wants *for* **O**ther or **S**takeholder (based on their interests). This is essential for collaboration.

Disclosing Wants:

- Eliminates hidden agenda.
- Does not guarantee that you will get all your wants, but puts them on the table for negotiation.
- Builds relationship by acknowledging and engaging others' interests.

6. STATE ACTIONS

State what you have done, are doing, or will do.

> "My mind was somewhere else, and I really didn't hear what you said."

> "I agree with what you have just said."

> "I promise not to kid you about that again."

Owning Your Own Behavior Says You Are:

- Aware
- Accountable (trustworthy)
- Responsible
- Committed

The Difference:

Recognize the difference between saying, "I might," "I could," or "I want to," and clearly committing yourself to Future Action, by saying "I will." Commitment to act distinguishes Skill # 6 (committed actions) from Skill # 5 (more tentative wants, wishes and desires).

USE THE TALKING SKILLS IN ANY ORDER

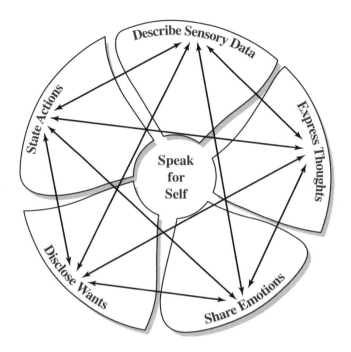

- The skills are numbered (on preceding pages) for convenient identification, not for use in a sequence. Apply them in any order as you share information about yourself.

- An effective message does not need to be lengthy. Use the talking skills to send multi-part messages — three or more zones of your Awareness Wheel in 30 seconds or less.

- A multi-part message is much clearer than a message that goes on and on in one zone.

INTUITION

Intuition is the experience of putting your Awareness Wheel together quickly and congruently. The Wheel also enables you to document the zones of your intuitions more specifically and share them with others more clearly.

CARING ABOUT YOURSELF

Consider These Summary Points:

- Self-awareness is an important resource you bring to any issue or situation.

- Self-awareness and self-disclosure are two different processes. Self-awareness is essential. Self-disclosure is a choice.

- The more parts of your Wheel you disclose, the clearer your message.

- Self-awareness increases self-control.

- You can use your Awareness Wheel to reduce stress, manage tension, and resolve issues by auguring deeper into your awareness.

- Connecting with all parts of your experience integrates fragmented information and releases blocked energy, which helps generate constructive future actions.

- Partial awareness yields poor outcomes.

- Fear and self-doubt block information and action.

- Knowing yourself is not the same as being selfish and self-centered.

- Caring behavior matches your experience with congruent words and actions, creating energy, strength, and health.

- Wherever you go, you can use your Awareness Wheel. To use it, ask yourself, "What am I experiencing right now?"

Tips:

- Expand awareness before taking action.

- Increase your choices with self-awareness/information.

- Ask yourself, "Are my actions (what I say and do) consistent with all parts of my Awareness Wheel?"

LEARNING AND APPLICATION TOOLS

The tools, which are part of your CORE Packet, can help you with practice for taking the high road during a conversation. They can assist you in learning and applying the CORE COMMUNICATION concepts, skills, and processes.

Awareness Wheel Pad

The Awareness Wheel pad has a number of uses. Suggestions include:

- Thinking through an issue alone (self-talk) by writing your experiences regarding the issue in the various zones.

- Preparing for an important conversation (with another person) by filling out the zones that relate or that you want to cover. Remember, self awareness is essential. Disclosure is a choice.

- "Standing in someone else's shoes" — filling out an Awareness Wheel on what you believe someone else is experiencing (prior to having a conversation with that person).

Pocket Card Set

This card set is a quick reference and a prompt for your skill practice and application. Keep it where it is handy for you.

The Laptop Mat

The Awareness Wheel is on one half of this mat.

- When you practice the talking skills with another person, use the laptop mat (Awareness Wheel side) to prompt self-awareness and skill use.

Awareness Wheel Floor Mat

The Awareness Wheel floor mat can be applied in several ways in addition to its use in a class. These include:

- Thinking through an issue alone (self-talk) when you do not want to sit and write but would rather be up moving about.

- Rehearsing your part of an important, upcoming conversation with someone.

- Prompting the talking skills as you share your awareness about an issue with someone (if you are comfortable using the mat in front of the person).

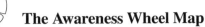

HOW TO OBSERVE AND COACH PROCESS — USING THE AWARENESS WHEEL FLOOR MAT

When you are the observer-coach (in a class, for example) for someone who is moving about the Awareness Wheel floor skills mat, sharing his or her awareness:

- Look for accuracy.
- Notice if statements match zones. Examples of mismatches include:
    — Feel instead of think — "I feel that we should . . ."
    — Want *from* other, instead of a clear want *for* other
    — Action (my behavior) versus sensory data (observations of others' actions)
- Notice which parts of the Wheel are covered or omitted.

To Coach:

Prior to a person beginning his or her story on the mat, ask whether he or she wants coaching during the exercise. If so, coach. If not, do not coach.

- Focus on process: Coach *process* — about the zones of the Information Wheel rather than about *content* or *outcome* (solutions).
- For a mismatch: Simply point with your foot, aligning the talker with the zone he or she is expressing.

Giving Feedback:

When the "talker" completes his or her story on the mat, ask if he or she would like some feedback. If so, give feedback. If not, do not.

- Start with positive feedback about parts a person does well.
- For missing information:
    • Say, for instance, "I noticed that you did not mention your emotions. (Do not have the person actually fill in the information. Just note it.)
    • If a person misses the future action, point it out, but do not pressure him or her to take any specific action. Sometimes a person is just trying to understand an issue/situation; commitment to future action comes later.

Coaching Tips

- Let each person tell his or her own issue, in the sequence and at the pace the individual chooses.
- Make coaching brief and specific, so the talker does not lose momentum.
- Be careful not to start directing — especially with questions.

SOMEONE I WANT TO INFLUENCE — REVISITED

Instruction

1. Recall the exercise on page xi at the beginning of this workbook, "Someone I Want to Influence" (about something of importance to you). Remember who the person is and what it is that you want to talk to him or her about.

2. Take four minutes and prepare again for the conversation. This time however, use the Awareness Wheel (below) to stimulate and organize what you want to say to this person.

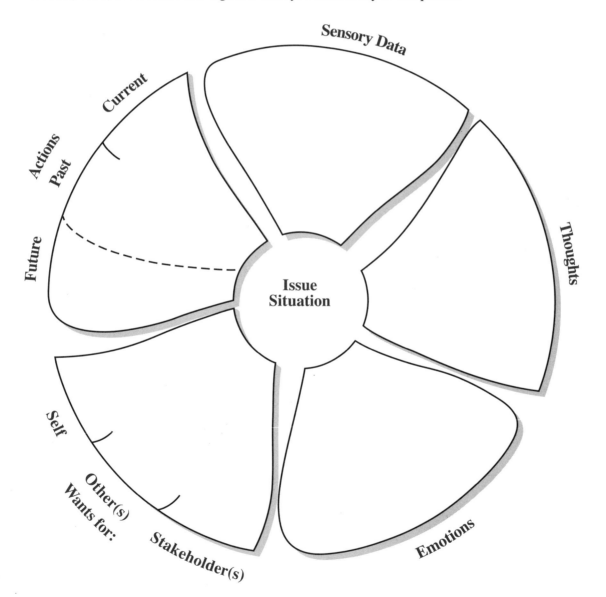

3. Code the Pre-Assessment: Turn again to page xi near the beginning of the workbook and code each of your original statements on the page with an S=Sensory Data, T=Thought, E=Emotions, W=Want, and A=Action.

4. Compare: How many and which zones of the Wheel did you cover in your first worksheet? Between the two exercises, how does the quality of information compare?

5. Think about the person you want to influence in terms of zones of the Awareness Wheel. With which zones do you believe he or she is most comfortable and probably the most likely to be able to hear, in order to respond favorably to your message?

6. Number the zones of the Awareness Wheel (representing the content in them) in the order which you believe would be most effective in the discussion.

7. Pick a time and place to talk to this person.

MY USE OF TALKING SKILLS

Instructions

Mark each item twice: first with an X for your typical behavior; next with an O for desired practice.

When you have a important conversation with another person, how often do you:

	Almost never				Very often	
1. Speak for self?	1	2	3	4	5	6
2. Speak for other (tell person what he/she should think, feel, want, or do)?	1	2	3	4	5	6
3. Describe sensory data (say what you observe)?	1	2	3	4	5	6
4. Express your thoughts?	1	2	3	4	5	6
5. Share your emotions?	1	2	3	4	5	6
6. Disclose your wants for self?	1	2	3	4	5	6
7. Disclose your wants for (not from) others?	1	2	3	4	5	6
8. State your current or past actions (own your behavior)?	1	2	3	4	5	6
9. State your future actions (make commitments, promises)?	1	2	3	4	5	6
10. Say one thing, but think, feel, want, or do another?	1	2	3	4	5	6

Action Plan

Circle the numbers of one or two skill-items to focus on improving.

TALKING SKILLS IDENTIFICATION

Instructions: Each of the fifteen statements below combines the skill "speaking for self" with one of the five zones of the Awareness Wheel, resulting in one of the other talking skills. Identify the talking skill in each statement by placing the letter for the skill on the line provided.

a) Describe Sensory Data

b) Express Thoughts

c) Share Emotions

d) Disclose Wants

e) State Actions

Answer

1. I'd like to arrange a time for the two of us to meet together. _____

2. I am really frustrated that I just missed my connecting flight. _____

3. I think this is an important step for me. _____

4. Wow, I'm thrilled to hear that news! _____

5. I expect the report will be ready at the end of the week. _____

6. I didn't get in touch with him. _____

7. I notice you got up and looked out the window. _____

8. I believe this is an accurate assessment. _____

9. I will pick you up at one o'clock tomorrow. _____

10. I'm sad to learn about her illness. _____

11. I wish I could visit her soon. _____

12. I smell freshly baked cookies. _____

13. I hope to go with them. _____

14. I'm looking for my phone right now. _____

15. I heard him say at lunch that he wanted to go with us. _____

The answers are:

1.d, 2.c, 3.b, 4.c, 5.b, 6.e, 7.a, 8.b, 9.e, 10.c, 11.d, 12.a, 13.d, 14.e, 15.a

CHANGING FIGHT AND SPITE TALK TO AWARE TALK

Instructions: Each of the ten statements below is an example of Fight Talk or Spite Talk. Use the space between statements to change the message into Aware Talk.

1. "You always have such stupid ideas. You're an idiot."

2. "You're always late. Can't you ever be on time?"

3. "You're a jerk. Just leave."

4. "Whatever you say, since you're such a genius."

5. "If I were as smart as you, I would have seen the mistake."

6. "Tell me again about how good you are, so I can get ready to cheer."

7. "No, nothing's wrong. What makes you think that?"

8. "Nobody ever invites me to go anywhere."

9. "You're rude and thoughtless."

Some possible Aware Talk statements for the sentences above include the following:

1. "I think your idea is unrealistic, and I'm afraid to try it."
2. "I get frustrated and angry when you don't arrive at the time we agreed upon."
3. "I'm really annoyed by your behavior, and I'd like time alone to think."
4. "I have a different idea about how we could approach this. Can we talk about an another option?"
5. "I didn't see the mistake."
6. "I hear lots of energy in your voice, and I think you're really excited about this."
7. "Yes, I am upset. I think I'm being discounted."
8. "I'd like to be included this time."
9. "In this situation, I think your comments discouraged him, rather than encouraged him to do something different."

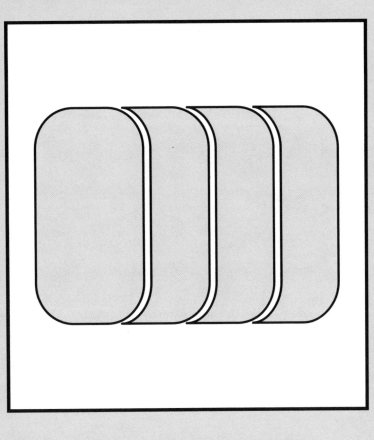

4

AWARENESS OF OTHERS

Every Body Communicates — Nonverbally
Rapport — Being in Sync
Hot or Cold

Effective interpersonal communication takes more than self-awareness and clarity of talking. It also requires that you *attend* to other people's feedback and *adjust* your own behavior so that you can connect and exchange information. Depending on your effectiveness with these processes, you build or dampen relationships.

Your level of awareness of others makes the difference in your ability to attend and adjust. You can think of your other-awareness as operating like a complex servo-mechanism that traverses new, uncharted, and or even difficult terrain by scanning the environment for feedback and adjusting its approach.

EVERY BODY COMMUNICATES — NONVERBALLY

As you relate to someone, in any style of communication, the other person responds to you. (And you in turn respond to him or her — no one cannot *not* communicate.) Besides verbally interacting, each person's body constantly "speaks" through subtle and not-so-subtle nonverbals, such as small facial changes, gestures, head movements and posture shifts; other nonverbals include rate, pitch, volume, and tone of voice.

Most nonverbals are spontaneous and hard to control consciously. They often reflect emotion and operate outside the sender's awareness. However, these nonverbal behaviors from others serve as your interpersonal sensory data base — your feedback.

Body Signature

Everyone has a *body signature* — a reoccurring pattern or range of large and small nonverbal behaviors that are unique to that person. For example, some people, who are quite expressive, tend to use more space around them and large gestures to communicate. Other less expressive people are more contained or subdued in their use of space and in their gestures. Their nonverbals are more subtle.

As you get to know someone, you come to recognize the body signature — his or her individual pattern of nonverbal behaviors. For instance, you notice the nonverbal cues in the person associated with calm, stressful, or exciting situations.

Points About Nonverbal Messages

Consider these points as you make use of nonverbal information from others in your exchanges.

- *Nonverbals come first.* People will show you their response before they tell it. For example, when you ask a question, if you watch as well as listen, you will typically see the answer (head movement) before you hear it.

- *Nonverbals are more powerful than verbals.* Observers usually believe what they see more than what they hear (in words), whether or not the interpretation of visual data is accurate.

- *Nonverbals are implicit; words are explicit.* Nonverbals signal what the response is, while words define what it is.

- *Nonverbals punctuate interaction.* They often suggest beginnings, endings, and recycling of short interactions.

Keep in Mind:

- *Nonverbals are easy to misinterpret.* No gesture by itself has a specific meaning. Every gesture can have multiple meanings. And, no one gesture means the same thing every time. Nonverbals depend in large part on context. For example, crossed "closed" arms can mean, "I'm not interested," or "I'm sitting on a chair without comfortable arm rests," or perhaps "It's cold in here and I'm hugging myself to stay warm." When you do not understand something you see nonverbally, ask for clarification.

- *Nonverbals serve as the basis for judging congruence.* A match or mismatch can occur between communication channels — between what a person says (verbally) and does (nonverbally). When a mismatch seems to be going on, check it out.

Attending to others' nonverbals (such as their smiling, frowning, head nodding, changes in breathing, or small movements of pulling back or leaning forward) provides you with much of the feedback you need for choosing, calibrating, or altering your own communication.

RAPPORT — BEING IN SYNC

The most important on-going dynamic between two people is rapport. When two individuals are in sync — in alignment, similarity, accord, commonality — you can see it first in their bodies (similar posture and nonverbal behavior) or in a common language (use of similar jargon or metaphors). They mirror or reflect each other in basic and subtle ways. Their physical movements and words seem to connect, displaying trust and liking.

On the other hand, when two people are out of sync, they lack basic rapport with each other. Again, you can see it in their bodies and behavior. They do not match. Rather, they seem to grate on each other — creating dissonance and distrust as they attempt to relate in awkward, uncertain, uncomfortable and uncoordinated ways. They seem out of step with one another and on different wave lengths.

People can mirror and match each other verbally and nonverbally in any style of communication. You will see both style shifts and changes in physical rapport as people:

- Negotiate the style in which they are going to relate.
- Change the topic.
- Encounter sudden dissonance between them.

Generally, most of us enjoy living, working, and playing with people with whom we share a high level of rapport. However, when these things do not go well, it is necessary to regain rapport.

Interactive Guideline: Establish and Maintain Rapport

When you want to influence someone or successfully meet new people, establish and then maintain rapport.

To establish rapport:

- First, look for ways to signal sameness and reduce difference (regardless of age, gender, race, ethnicity, and so on). For example, notice speech rate or posture.
- Then, to come into sync, literally match (mirror or reflect, but not mimic) another person's behavior (verbal or nonverbal), such as alter your speech rate or posture.

In these ways, align yourself by taking your cues from the other person. Once you are in alignment (which usually takes just a few seconds), often the two of you begin to blend — mirroring and matching each other naturally. In fact, when someone is connecting with you, you can see him or her unconsciously mirroring your own behavior as well.

When rapport is established, your behavior unconsciously suggests things such as: "We're alike." "You can trust me." "We're on the same side." "I like you."

When you realize you have lost rapport with someone, consciously mirror and match again to reestablish your rapport.

Points to Consider

- It takes only a moment to align yourself physically with another person, before you engage yourself fully in the conversation.

- High rapport does not necessarily mean agreement. You can disagree with someone and still be in sync. For example, two people can disagree in Aware Talk and still experience rapport with one another.

- Rapport is hardest to establish with people most unlike you or with people to whom you find it difficult to relate. It develops quite naturally with people most like you.

- Sometimes the people you want to influence the most are people with whom you have the least rapport.

Results of Mirroring Others

Intentionally mirroring others will:

- Prevent you from sending negative nonverbal messages.
- Take the attention off yourself in awkward or new situations.
- Help you understand and sometimes share another person's experience.
- Enable you to avoid overpowering or underpowering the other.
- Reduce interpersonal dissonance.
- Build relationship.

Suggestions

1. Look for and build on similarities, likeness, and common ground with others. If you focus primarily on differences, your body and nonverbals will communicate rejection.

2. Match someone's words and images. Everyone has his or her own vocabulary.

3. In a meeting, mirror and match the body language of the person you want to influence (to increase your similarity and reduce difference or dissonance)

HOT OR COLD

An old-fashioned children's game used to be called "Hot or Cold," "Hide the Thimble," or something similar. The rules were simple: Someone left the room and the other people hid an object. When the individual re-entered the room, he or she was supposed to find the hidden object based on the verbal feedback the others in the room provided.

As the seeker moved closer to the hidden object, the others called out, "Warm!" "Hot!" or (very close) "Burning up!" If the person moved away from the object, the others would say, "You're cold!" "Ice cold!" or "Freezing!"

The game was fun, and the seeker would readily find the object as long as he or she:

> 1) Was given accurate feedback.

> 2) Attended to and used the feedback.

If the seeker was given inaccurate information by others or did not attend to the feedback, the game became a frustrating random search without helpful information.

Interpersonal communication operates on a feedback system very much like playing the game "Hot or Cold." Other people's nonverbals are the hot and cold feedback that give you clues as to whether what you are doing in the conversation is effective or not. The nonverbals suggest if your actions are receiving a:

- Positive (hot) response — consideration, acceptance, agreement
- Negative (cold) response — reluctance, rejection, disagreement

Others' nonverbals translate to "warm," "hot," "sizzling," or "cool," "cold," "freezing," respectively.

As you interact with someone, the other person's nonverbals often reflect the impact of your communication. They are as much a statement about you — as they are a statement about the other person.

Interactive Guideline: Watch the Hot or Cold Nonverbals

You can generally make safe and useful global judgments about how you are doing in the interaction from the other person's hot or cold nonverbal responses to you. Adjust accordingly. However, since nonverbals are implicit and not explicit, be careful not to read too much explicitness into them. Do not make detailed interpretations of the nonverbals.

EXERCISE: ATTENDING TO NONVERBALS

Instructions: Choose someone to observe over the next few days whom you are likely to see in both *calm* and *pressured* situations. In each circumstance, notice the subtle differences you observe in the nonverbal behavior, for example, breathing, facial expressions (including lower lip), gestures, posture, speech rate, voice tone and volume, and use of space. Record some of your observations below.

EXERCISE: OBSERVING RAPPORT

Instructions: Find a situation where you see two people (perhaps by people-watching in a public place) who seem obviously to be in sync with one another — they look as though they are really connected. Look at similar body posture or behaviors that mirror or match one another. Describe their behavior.

EXERCISE: NOTICE HOT AND COLD

Instructions: Look for an opportunity to experience someone using Control Talk with another person or other people. Observe the non-verbal behavior of the other(s). Describe what is said and the nonverbal (hot versus cold) responses to it. What visual or voice expressions do you see and hear in the responders?

5

THE LISTENING CYCLE MAP

Styles of Listening
Use of Questions in Listening
5 Listening Skills

In the same way that self-awareness is important for clearer communication between you and another person, so is understanding him or her well, especially when you have a serious conversation. Effective listening — an important element of other-awareness — is the key to that understanding .

Many times listening is simply a way to connect with and enjoy someone else. At other times, listening concerns a decision or disagreement that arises between you and another person. In these cases, how you listen takes on greater significance. For building and maintaining satisfying and good relationships, listening skills become essential.

This chapter describes styles of listening characteristic of, or appropriate for, various situations and then provides specific skills for times when deep listening is required.

> Different styles of listening create corresponding levels
> of information, trust, and connectedness.

STYLES OF LISTENING

The key to effective listening is to manage yourself by using listening styles appropriate to the situation. The diagram below shows these styles as they fit into the Communication Styles Map (as introduced on page 14 in Chapter 1).

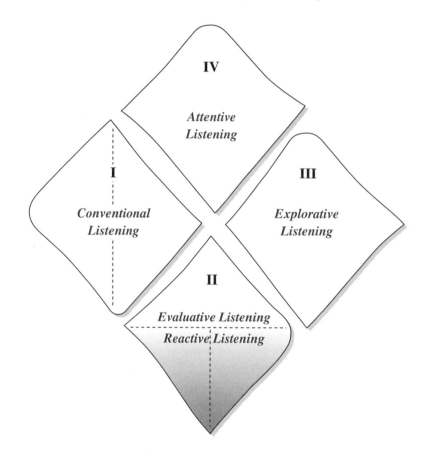

- Style I — Conventional Listening is appropriate for relaxed or routine exchanges.

- Style II — Evaluative/Reactive Listening operates from a closed (right or wrong, good or bad) position. It fits when you want selective information to make a quick reaction.

- Style III — Explorative Listening uses questions to probe for information.

- Style IV — Attentive Listening creates understanding — takes you to the heart of a matter.

Your styles of communication — how you talk and listen — determine the quality of information exchanged and the state of your relationship with that person. After describing Styles I and II, this chapter focuses primarily on the listening skills associated with Styles III and IV, the two best listening styles for resolving issues with others in important, complicated, or conflicted situations.

STYLE I — CONVENTIONAL LISTENING

Conventional Listening is the way you typically show interest in Small Talk or Shop Talk. You connect and make yourself available in a pleasant, sociable way.

In Conventional Listening, you:

- Serve as a relaxed sounding board for chit chat and stories.
- Gather Shop Talk information.
- Ask questions of a general nature or respond non-verbally on a light level to keep the exchange going.
- May listen half-heartedly to signal your wish to shift the conversation to something more substantial, or exit the conversation.

Associational Listening

When a talker's conversation reminds you (the listener) of a similar situation, topic, or experience, instead of continuing to listen, you respond by moving to talking about your own experience. The move can be positive or negative, for example:

- Positive, when everyone joins in, trading stories, laughing and enjoying each other's contribution, which energizes and keeps a conversation going.
- Negative, when it becomes a take-away — a disruption or distraction from the other person's point or story. This is particularly true when the other person is trying to say something serious and important.

Impact of Conventional Listening

This listening style:

- Contributes to a relaxing time together.
- Keeps a conversation going and routine matters known.
- Can trigger annoyance if the talker wants a deeper response.
- Is less conducive to discovering critical information.

STYLE II — EVALUATIVE AND REACTIVE LISTENING

In this style, you listen in a way that tries to control the path of the conversation. As you do so, you take an evaluative stance, listening to hear if the other person discloses information that is useful or not to you, or with which you agree or disagree. While the intensity of your evaluating can vary, your behavior can become anxious or defensive, and then you slide easily into being reactive. You attempt to squelch and counter information that does not fit what you are listening for or your point of view.

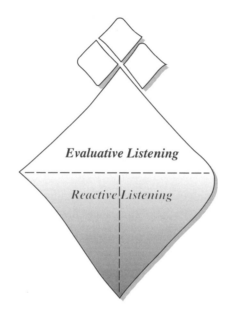

Examples of Evaluative and Reactive Listening Behaviors:

Judging, such as: "That's right, wrong, good, bad, smart, foolish."

Internally rehearsing a rebuttal

Interrupting with statements or challenging questions to take over the conversation and dispute a point

Listening selectively, disattending to, ignoring critical information

Assuming, mind-reading, projecting (your experience on other)

Asking questions to cover your own hidden agenda: "Don't you think. . . ?"

Using "Why" questions that call for justification and imply blame

Interrogating: "Tell me what you're thinking. Speak up!"

Crowding (aggressive) or *disengaging* (distancing) *gestures when the other is talking*

Ignoring, twisting, distorting, or manipulating what the talker says in an attempt to force agreement or change

Impacts of Evaluative and Reactive Listening

Positive Aspects

On the positive side, this listening style can energize an exchange and even stimulate action. For example, when time is short and a quick decision must be made, you listen long enough to get information significant to you, and then take control. As you do so, others go along with you.

Negative Aspects

Often however, the impacts of using Style II listening behaviors are negative, especially when someone is trying to explain his or her side of things. In these cases, the listening style is inefficient and generates anger and frustration, yielding unsatisfactory results. Disagreements quickly become power struggles rather than information exchanges (with anyone involved vying for who is right or wrong). Lack of listening skills leaves people stuck.

Typically, the style:

- Shows an attitude of discounting the talker — "I count, you don't."
- Signals resistance.
- Generates stress — tension, frustration, anger, and defensiveness.
- Undermines rapport and trust.
- Spawns fragmented, inaccurate, and misleading information.
- Prolongs the resolution process and results in poor decisions.
- Runs the risk of creating bad feelings and of damaging relationships.

When you listen evaluatively and reactively, you keep yourself front and center, focusing attention more on your own experience rather than on the other person's. This lessens your ability to gain awareness of the other's perspective, which could be important in making a decision that affects you and others in your SOS relationship system.

> Am I really listening or
> just anxiously waiting to talk?

STYLE III — EXPLORATIVE LISTENING

Explorative Listening is a style used to search for and increase significant information regarding complex or non-routine issues and situations. Through the use of questions, this style develops perspective.

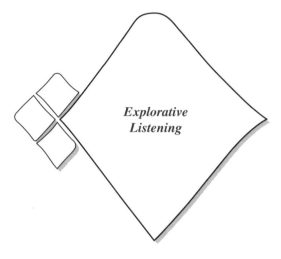

Explorative Listening

Explorative Listening Behaviors

In this style, questions are used for:

Getting a conversation started

Influencing/Guiding the conversation

Probing for information in a non-accusatory fashion

Gaining/Expanding information or perspective

Filling in missing or unclear parts of the Awareness Wheel

Clarifying misunderstandings

Clearing up confusion

Confirming information

Generating possibilities

Seeking advice

Making Requests

"Testing the water"

Types of Questions

The structure of a question limits or expands the kind and quality of information disclosed by the talker. One form generates either-or kinds of answers. The other form elicits broader or more widely extended, open-ended kinds of answers, and this form is referred to as an open question.

Either-Or Questions

Questions that begin with a "being verb" — is, are, do, was, did, has, have, could, would, will — stimulate an either-or answer. Often the questions call for a "Yes" or "No" answer, though other types of either-or answers occur, as well. For example:

> *"Do you have enough gas for the drive there?"* (yes or no)
>
> *"Are you happy with your decision?"* (yes or no)
>
> *"Will you follow up with a phone call?"* (yes or no)

While either-or questions are efficient, they also narrow information. They are most often used in Styles I and II.

Open Questions

By adding "Who," "What," "Where," "When," or "How," to a "being verb," you create an "open question." Open questions have the potential of gaining more information.

For example:

> *"Who was* at their house?" or *"Where is* it?"(data zone)
>
> *"What do* you think about that?"(thought zone)
>
> *"How are* you feeling about the decision?" (emotion zone)
>
> *"When would* you like to go?" (want zone)
>
> *"What will* you do?" (action zone)

Caution

Notice that "Why" is not included. Although "Why" is a good research question, it is often used to blame or demand justification (Reactive Listening). On the other hand, questions beginning with "Who," "What," "Where," "When," and "How," gain information about "Why" without the negative implications.

Tone also influences the response. If you use a negative tone, you can easily turn an open question into a reactive challenge.

Use The Awareness Wheel to Guide Open Questions

Most people ask questions (probe) randomly, hoping to tap into a useful piece of information that will be helpful. They have no map to guide their questioning. Besides being a map for talking, the Awareness Wheel is also a listening map, a guide for you to gain useful information effectively. The map will help you organize information, as well as fill in missing information.

To form a focused open question, combine "Who," "What," "Where," "When," and "How," (but not "Why") with any zone of the Awareness Wheel.

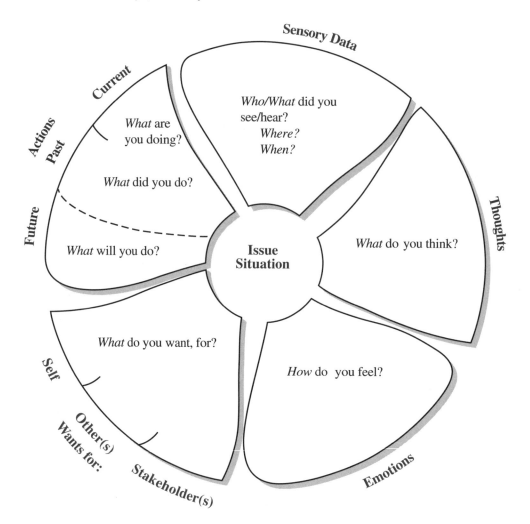

ASKING OPEN QUESTIONS

Instructions

For questioner: Use Open Questions to fill out an Awareness Wheel as you interview someone about an event or issue of importance to him or her. Use the Wheel (below) as a guide for asking the questions and making notes as you fill out his or her experience.

For observers: As you observe the conversation, use a sheet from your Awareness Wheel pad to record your observations.

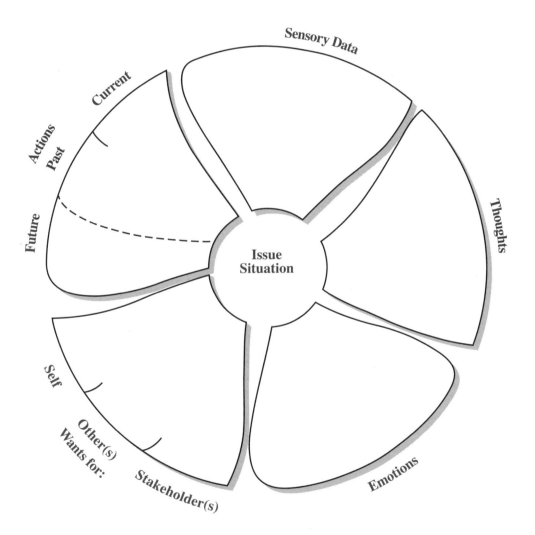

Special Use of Explorative Listening

Open questions are particularly useful in guiding a conversation with people who:

Talk *too little* — need prompting to tell their story completely.

Talk *too much* — need organization to help them focus.

Positive Impacts of Explorative Listening Using Open Questions

Open questions focus the conversation. They are used to facilitate:

- Brainstorming
- Decision-making
- Issue exploration
- Problem solving
- Conflict resolution

Negative Impacts of Asking Questions, Even Open Questions

Questions, intentionally or unintentionally, run the risk of:

- Disrupting the spontaneous flow of a talker's story.
- Leading the conversation away from critical information.
- Shifting the focus from the talker's source experience to the listener's interests (agenda) or experience.
- Anticipating the next questions, rather than attending to immediate data.

Notice — All Questions Lead

As a listener asks questions to gain information, knowingly or unknowingly, he or she directs and influences — leads — the conversation. Since questions come out of the asker's mind (experience and agenda) and not necessarily from that of the responder, all questions lead. This may or may not be helpful. Be aware that questions can unintentionally (or intentionally) mis-direct or pre-close a conversation and get in the way of discovering critical information.

Put Questions To Good Use — Do Not Let Them Get In The Way

- *Think about when to ask questions.* People often ask questions too early and too much in a listening situation. (Many people think listening means solving problems, so their job as a listener is to guide the talker to a solution, or come up with the answer. As a result, they over-direct or easily lapse into giving advice.)

- *Consider the necessity for questions.* Some people believe that they show their interest in a problem by taking over the conversation with questions. As a result, they often frustrate the talker.

Points About Questions (Whether Either-Or or Open Questions)

- *Answers tend to be limited to what the questions ask.* This can create the situation later in which the listener asks (blaming), "Why didn't you tell me that earlier?" The talker replies (also blaming), "I don't know. You never asked me."

- *Questions can place too much responsibility on the listener,* rather than allowing the talker to lead the listener to key information.

- *The value of a question is determined by the quality of information it produces.*

QUESTIONS ABOUT YOUR OWN LISTENING BEHAVIOR

How is your listening in a conversation with someone when:

- An issue exists in which you both have a stake?
- The other person wants to share his or her experience of an important event or idea?
- The other person seeks your advice?
- Conflict has erupted.

In these situations:

- To what extent do you inhibit, contaminate, allow, or encourage another's information?
- Is your intent typically to control the conversation (make sure you get the kind of information you want) or to connect with the other person?
- Do you listen for *agreement* or to pursue *understanding* (on which to build agreement)?

Explorative Listening works best in combination with the next style of listening, to get to the heart of a matter, to help build understanding, and to take action.

LISTENING FOR AGREEMENT OR UNDERSTANDING

Most people are not particularly good listeners in situations that are complicated or under pressure. A major reason for this is that people mainly *listen to agree or disagree* with each other, rather than *to understand* each other. Internally they are evaluating what is being said, thinking, "That's right" or "That's wrong." And when they disagree, they usually counter with their own point. The process feeds conflict and easily escalates differences into stressful, unresolved impasses.

You can learn how to prevent impasses and resolve them when they occur. This is particularly helpful in important, complicated, or conflicted situations. With skills, you can transcend *listening for agreement* and add more value by *listening for understanding*. This will allow you to gain useful, significant information As a result, you will make better decisions and create more satisfying relationships.

Agreement is very important and often a necessary outcome if two or more people are involved in a decision. However, a big difference exists between *forcing agreements* and *building agreements*. Forcing agreements breeds its own resistance, limitations, and failures. Listening to build agreements develops mutual buy-in and more pleasing outcomes. This requires effective listening skills for discovering important information.

STYLE IV — ATTENTIVE LISTENING

Attentive Listening engages the talker, encouraging him or her to speak freely and fully about his or her experience. This style of listening fosters the flow and quality of information without the listener agreeing, disagreeing, or directing the conversation.

The Goal: To Understand

To reach understanding, you seek to:

- *Hear* in an uncontaminated way, another person's "story."
- *Comprehend* his or her experience accurately.
- *Discover* useful information.

When you listen attentively, your awareness of the other person increases, typically resulting in information that is essential for building agreements as you negotiate, make decisions, or resolve conflicts.

THE LISTENING CYCLE MAP: FIVE SKILLS

The Listening Cycle is a map of listening skills, providing a guide for applying the skills. With its use, you can maximize your ability to listen for understanding.

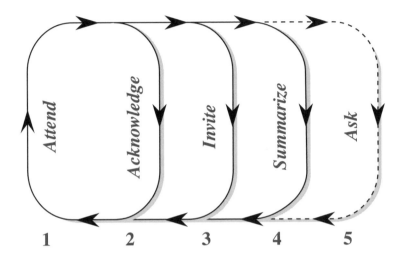

The first four skills of The Listening Cycle make up the Attentive Listening style:

    1. Attend — Look, Listen, and Track

    2. Acknowledge — Other's Experience

    3. Invite — More Information

    4. Summarize — to Ensure Accuracy

The fifth skill of Asking Open Questions, a major part of the Explorative Listening Style, is presented earlier in this chapter:

    5. Ask — Open Questions

The following pages describe how to use the first four skills.

> The secret to building agreements is
> to listen first for understanding.

ATTENTIVE LISTENING SKILLS

1. ATTEND — Look, Listen, Track

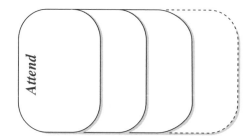

Attending means *paying complete attention* to the talker (not multi-tasking — internally or externally), *being fully present* to his or her experience. This is a foundational listening skill.

As you listen with an open, inviting body posture, you allow yourself to sense the other's non-verbal emotional signals (mainly in his or her face), as well as to the words being spoken. As you synchronize with the person, you gain emotional understanding — a connection called empathy — as well as an intellectual understanding of his or her thoughts, feelings and wants.

How to Attend:

- *Take a calming breath.*

- *Observe* the talker's nonverbals — shifts in posture, facial expression, tension and energy. (Watch the hot and cold nonverbals, as introduced in Chapter 4.)

- *Listen* to the sounds of the voice — tone, pitch, pace, and volume of speech.

- *Track* the talker's Awareness Wheel — the content of what he or she says in terms of the zones of the Wheel. (See the graphic on the next page.)

Attending Tips

- Set your own concerns aside temporarily.

- Stop other activity that is, or could appear to be, distracting.

- Mirror the talker (sit/sit; stand/stand).

- Make eye contact as you listen.

- Let the talker set the pace (be the leader of the conversation). This signals your availability, receptivity, and interest.

To Track:

Follow what the talker says according to the zones of the Awareness Wheel.

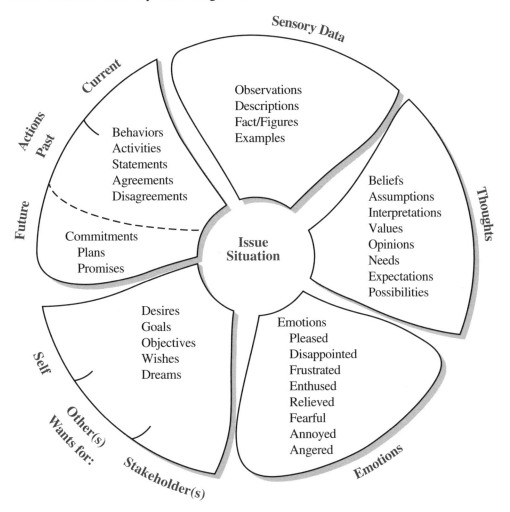

The Awareness Wheel provides a map that allows you to track the content of a conversation. As you track:

■ Notice the zones covered and those not addressed.

■ Watch for congruence/incongruence — the match between the person's words and his or her nonverbals. (For example, the person says, "I'm pleased" and looks pleased; or says, "I'm happy" but looks or sounds disappointed.)

Later you can ask open questions to fill in missing zones. Or you can disclose your own experience in a particular zone.

2. ACKNOWLEDGE — Other's Experience

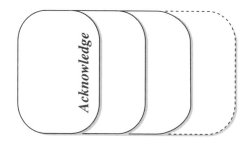

Acknowledgements are distillations — one or two words or a brief phrase — that you speak while the other person is talking, which capture accurately what he or she is saying and expressing nonverbally. For example:

"Challenging."

"New Opportunity."

"Frustrating."

How to Acknowledge

"Voice over" accurately, by coming in micro-seconds *behind* (following) the talker; *not ahead* (leading), which would be putting words into his or her mouth.

Acknowledging Tips

- Go beyond your nonverbal supportive facial expressions and sounds to verbalize explicitly what the talker is expressing.

- Move to where the talker is — data, thoughts, emotions, wants, actions — rather than where your urges are as a listener.

- Do not wait for the talker to pause, rather verbalize as the talker speaks. (When done well, these acknowledgements do not disrupt the talker but rather energize him or her. They act like sonar, confirming that you are on target. If you are off course, the talker will correct or calibrate your understanding.)

- Tune into the other person's experience and do not superimpose (project) your experience on him or her.

- Watch the talker's face for small nonverbals, such as nods and smiles or frowns and blank stares. They will signal the accuracy (or inaccuracy) of your understanding. When you touch the right chord, the talker will be energized. If you are off track, you will see it in his or her hot or cold facial expressions and other nonverbals.

- Listen carefully and express unstated *emotions* and *wants*:

  Sore spots — anger, frustration (negative energy)

  Soft spots — fear, hurt, vulnerability

  Unfulfilled expectations

  Blocked wants, desires

  Hot spots — excitement

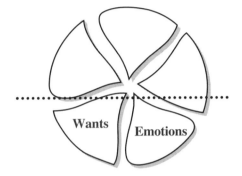

When You Acknowledge Someone, You:

- Show respect for and acceptance of his or her experience as being valid and legitimate for him or her. (This does not necessarily mean you agree. Your experience may be totally different.)
- Deepen connection with, and comprehension of, the other's experience.
- Demonstrate that the person has your moment-to-moment full attention and understanding.

Points About the Skill of Acknowledging

- Acknowledging confirms that you are following the other's story, and not sidetracking him or her with your concerns. You stand in the talker's shoes.
- Acknowledgements reduce the talker's anxiety by your offering no resistance.
- Acknowledging what the other person is experiencing, independent of whether you agree or disagree, is powerful. It is often all that is necessary to connect and create understanding.
- Attending and acknowledging build bridges. They show you care about the person, particularly significant when this is someone important to you, and you affirm his or her right to talk and be understood. These skills are strong forces for building relationship and establishing groundwork for collaboration.

3. INVITE — More Information

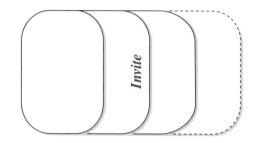

Inviting means that *you say or do something that encourages the talker to continue spontaneously talking about whatever it is he or she wants to tell you.* The effect of an invitation is that the talker, not the listener, chooses where to go next.

How to Invite:

■ Inviting can take three forms:

Gentle command:

"Continue."

"Say more."

Wide Open Question (rather than an open question, which focuses on a specific zone of the Wheel.):

"What else?"

"Anything more?"

Statement:

"I'd like to hear more."

"This is hard for me to hear, but I'd like you to continue."

Invite when:

■ There is a pause.

■ You experience the urge to react, disagree, or advise.

■ You want to ask a question.

Keep inviting — Two, Three, or More Times:

■ You will receive richer, more complete information.

■ Continue inviting until the talker says he or she has nothing more to add. At that point you know the story is complete, and that it is time for a summary (the next skill to be described) or for you to begin asking questions or talk yourself.

- Sometimes the talker will say he or she has nothing more to add, or will pause and go on to say, "But," and then give you a piece of informational gold.

Points About the Skill of Inviting

- Giving a person maximum choice and freedom to tell his or her side of things usually produces the richest information, most efficiently.

- Inviting is a particularly useful skill when the talker wants to tell his or her experience, but for various reasons, you are prone to direct or take over for him or her.

- Inviting, like peeling an onion a layer at a time, will take you deeper into the core of a person's experience.

- Essentially, each time you invite, you let the talker know, "What you are saying is important to me. I have time to listen. I want you to keep talking." As a result, most talkers relax, trust grows, and the person is more likely to tell you what is really going on — what he or she really thinks, feels, or wants.

- Typically, after receiving several invitations, the talker reveals information not yet said but important to the issue.

- Rather than playing a guessing game with questions, inviting lets the talker lead you to the critical information. Until he or she has no more to add, questions are premature and mainly distract and sidetrack.

- The skill of inviting operationalizes the 80/20 rule. As a listener, you encourage and allow the talker to connect with his or her own uncontaminated experience regarding an issue or situation.

> Quality listening means getting the whole story accurately, the first time.

4. SUMMARIZE — to Ensure Accuracy

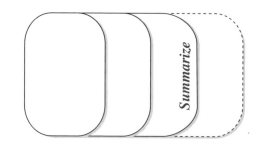

Summarizing means condensing a talker's message accurately. This demonstrates to the talker that you have understood accurately what he or she has said. It ensures that the message sent has been the message received, whether or not you agree with what the other has said.

How to Summarize:

- Condense in your own words what you have just heard to be the other person's points. It is often helpful to introduce your summary by stating, for example:

   "Let me see if I've got what you just said."

   "I'd like to run back what you've just told me to be sure I've got it."

- *Do not add to* (make inferences about) *or miss* important elements from the original message.

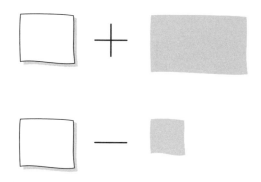

- Watch the talker's facial expression, such as nodding, smiling, or displaying other positive nonverbals, for a signal of accuracy. (Notice the hot or cold nonverbals.)

- Ask for confirmation or clarification of your summary if the talker's response is unclear, uncertain, or disconfirming.

■ Re-cycle a summary more than once until the talker and you are satisfied that the message received is an accurate, though condensed, representation of the message sent.

When to Summarize

It is useful to summarize at any point in a conversation when you:

Have an important issue at hand and believe understanding is critical

Think misunderstanding seems to be occurring

Experience a stressful exchange

Want to prioritize issues

Want to clarify perspectives

Do not want to miss something significant

Confirm an action plan

Points About the Skill of Summarizing

■ People like to be heard accurately. Summarizing builds confidence, trust, and relationship.

■ Interrupting someone to summarize his or her points is rarely seen as rude. Usually, quite the opposite, it is considered respectful.

■ Summarizing punctuates a complicated conversation, assuring understanding before proceeding.

■ A talker can ask the listener for a summary as well, without waiting for the listener to initiate one. ("Can you tell me what you've heard me say?")

Tip

Avoid saying, "I understand what you mean." (The statement is often used to take charge of or control of a conversation, without real understanding.) Rather, demonstrate your understanding with an accurate summary.

5. ASK — Open Questions

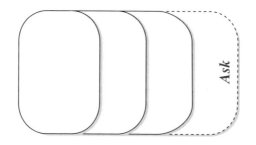

After you have helped a person tell you his or her concern or story as completely as possible using the Attentive Listening Skills 1 to 4 (described above), you may want to fill in missing information or clarify confusing parts. To do this, ask the open explorative questions of "Who," "What," "Where," "When," and "How." Consider asking questions from all the zones of the Awareness Wheel. For instance:

> "Who was there?"
>
> "What do you want for Jim (based on his interests)?"
>
> "Where do you think this will take place?"
>
> "How did you feel?"
>
> "When are you going?"

- Remember, all questions lead the conversation. The dotted line in the Listening Cycle around "Ask" means use questions wisely.

- The better you get at Attentive Listening, the less you need to ask questions. Most people will take you more quickly to the heart of critical information if you let them guide you.

- Questions are helpful when you want to guide, structure, or limit information. Usually though, if given the chance, most people tell their story best with acknowledgements and invitations rather than with probing questions.

APPLY THE LISTENING CYCLE

Listening for understanding (distinct from listening for agreement or disagreement) is a learned behavior. It does not come naturally. The Listening Cycle can help you listen for understanding.

The Listening Cycle guides and combines the skills for most effective listening. While each of the five skills can be used independently and in any order as you listen, you heighten your ability to understand another by combining the skills to continue following the talker. This is especially significant when you are discussing a *complex* or *stressful* issue.

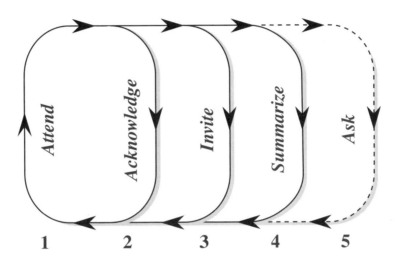

- Notice in the Listening Cycle, the solid lines that circulate among the Attentive Listening skills —Attend, Acknowledge, Invite, and Summarize. Recycling these skills, in any order, produces the highest quality of useable information possible.

- Ask (open questions) is positioned last and set off by dotted lines. This is to remind you to use questions wisely. The better you become at using the first four listening skills, the less you need to rely on questions.

- One combination of two skills, which is particularly useful when used in sequence, is:

    Summarize followed by Invite

POINTS ABOUT LISTENING

- Some people fear that the actual process of listening for understanding will be read by the talker as agreement, when in fact the listener is not in agreement. If this becomes a concern during a conversation, simply clarify that you are not in agreement but that you are trying to understand accurately the talker's perspective. (Then invite the talker to continue.)

- The Attentive Listening skills do not all have to be used together and at one time. More often, the skills are used separately and sprinkled throughout a conversation.

- Not all situations call for complete and full understanding. Use Styles of Listening flexibly.

- Being pre-occupied, self-absorbed, or feeling anxious interferes with the ability to listen for understanding.

- A big difference exists in productivity between a person or group who can listen to each other for understanding and a person or group who cannot.

Natural Behaviors:	Learned Skills:
Ignore	Attend
Interrupt	Acknowledge
Talk or Question	Invite
Assume	Summarize
Tell	Ask

CARING ABOUT OTHERS AND STAKEHOLDERS

When you use the Listening Cycle, you set your own concerns aside temporarily (typically you will not forget them) as you allow and encourage the other person to express his or her concerns fully. In the process, you demonstrate caring about or counting that person.

Some outcomes and benefits that you experience include:

- Getting to the center of issues faster with less interpersonal stress.

- Supporting (energizing) the talker to disclose and share critical information.

- Earning the right to be heard after you have listened to the other person tell his or her full story.

- Increasing your choices and influence. (Some people fear unnecessarily that if they listen for understanding they will lose control.)

- Relating more constructively to the other's legitimate concerns.

- Taking action after you have reached understanding

- Creating a collaborative atmosphere for building best-fit agreements based on understanding.

- Leaving the other person feeling good about you, which develops trust and builds relationships.

USE THE LAPTOP MAT

The Listening cycle is one part of this mat.

- When you practice the listening skills, use the laptop mat (Listening Cycle side) to prompt your use of skills.

HOW TO OBSERVE AND COACH PROCESS —
USING THE LISTENING CYCLE SKILLS MAT

To Coach: Prior to a listener using the Listening Cycle floor skills mat to listen to someone talk about an issue, ask whether he or she wants coaching during the exercise. If so, coach. If not, do not coach. Before you start the coaching:

- Make sure the mat is set so that the listener looks down on the words "Listening Cycle" (at the bottom). The skill words would be perpendicular to him or her.

- Ask the listener if you could fold under the mat the skill called "Ask Open Questions" for practice on the four other skills without questions.

- Suggest to the listener to dedicate one foot to step on each listening skill as he or she uses the skill. (This lets you see the skill he or she is intending to use.)

- Ask the listener to step on and return to "Attend" before and after using each of the other skills.

When you coach:

- Focus on *process* — the specific listening skills rather than either *content* or *outcome* (solutions).

- Watch for accuracy of skills use.

- Observe the talker's hot or cold nonverbals in response to the listener's skills.

- Prompt the listener to use specific listening skills by giving "verbal prompts." For example, say, "Acknowledge" or "Summarize" when you think it might be useful. (Avoid using your foot to prompt listening skills. In most situations, the listener will not notice your foot prompting if he or she is maintaining eye contact with the person talking. Also, verbal prompts give the listener a moment to respond, while foot prompts tend to elicit immediate responses.

Giving Feedback:

When the talker completes telling about his or her issue on the mat, ask him or her:

- How was it to be listened to in this way?

- How well were you understood by the listener?

Ask the listener if he or she would like some feedback. If so, give feedback. If not, do not.

- Start with positive feedback about parts the listener did well.

- Mention areas, if any, where you thought the skill was not accurate, and give an example of what could have been more useful.

- Comment on any specific hot or cold nonverbals in the talker (remember the talker is the authority on their impact) in response to specific skills.

MY LISTENING STYLES

Instructions

Step 1. Think of the listening styles you use when you are conversing with someone in your family, at work, or with a person important to you. Estimate the percentage of time you *typically* spend in each of the styles. Then, give a percent for your desired usage.

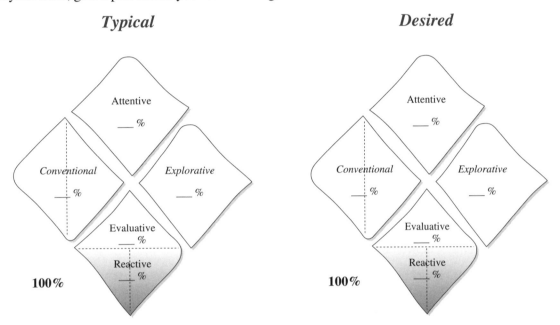

Typical   *Desired*

Step 2. Choose a listening style that would be particulary helpful to increase (circle it) and one to decrease (put an X through it).

Step 3. When and where will you implement these changes?

MY USE OF LISTENING SKILLS

Instructions

Mark each item twice: first with an X for the way you typically listen now and next with an O for your desired practice.

When you have a serious conversation with another person, how often do you:

	Almost never				Very often
1. Fake listening when pre-occupied?	1 2 3 4 5 6
2. Listen briefly, then take over the discussion, giving information or solutions?	1 2 3 4 5 6
3. React defensively?	1 2 3 4 5 6
4. Not take time to listen to the other's full information?	1 2 3 4 5 6
5. Direct the conversation with questions?	1 2 3 4 5 6
6. Attend to the other's nonverbals?	1 2 3 4 5 6
7. Acknowledge the other's experience?	1 2 3 4 5 6
8. Invite the other to continue talking?	1 2 3 4 5 6
9. Summarize the other's message to ensure accuracy and demonstrate understanding?	1 2 3 4 5 6
10. Ask Open Questions focused on zones in the Awareness Wheel?	1 2 3 4 5 6

Action Plan

Circle the number of one or two items to increase or decrease to improve your listening.

"BUT I DON'T HAVE TIME TO LISTEN ATTENTIVELY."

Sometimes people think they do not have enough time to listen attentively when issues arise. However, not taking time to listen carefully fosters lower quality information, and that can be costly (in terms of relationship or productivity). Attentive listening may take a few more minutes in the short run. In the long run, it produces better results. Consider the impact in the following situations:

1. Think of a situation you experienced in which someone did not take time to listen to you, or to another person, carefully. What was the impact on you, the other person, and any other stakeholders?

2. Think of a situation in which you did not take time to listen attentively. What was the impact on you, another person, and any stakeholders?

3. In what specific situations can you apply the Attentive Listening Skills?

USING THE LISTENING CYCLE

Instructions: In a situation in which you and another person are having a conversation, intentionally focus on using the four listening skills that are connected by the solid lines on the Cycle — the Attentive Listening Skills.

Afterwards, evaluate the impact of your use of the skills regarding:

- The general atmosphere between you.
- The quality of the information you gained.

Options:

With Another Generation

Look for an opportunity for when a younger person (a child perhaps) starts to request something. Intentionally use the Attentive Listening skills to connect with him or her. Notice the impact of the conversation on the younger person and on yourself.

Find an older person who would be interested in telling you something about himself or herself. Perhaps it would be a significant time in his or her life. Use the Attentive Listening skills simply to understand. Ask open questions sparingly and wisely.

With a Person of Another Political Perspective

Look for someone whose belief system is different from yours. Tell the person you would like to understand his or her point of view. Use the listening skills to understand (rather than to agree or disagree). If you believe the person thinks you are agreeing (and you are not), simply say you are not necessarily agreeing with him or her, but you do want to understand the perspective.

With a Person at Work, Another Family Member, or a Friend in a Stressful Situation

When a situation arises, use the Attentive Listening skills to understand clearly the person's perspective on what is happening. Use questions wisely. Notice how your skills influence the situation.

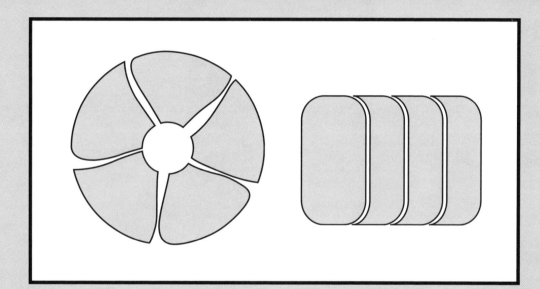

6

DEALING WITH CONFLICT

The Third Force in Conflict
Styles and Processes
Your Conflict Patterns

As you live your life and interact with others, no doubt from time to time, you find yourself in a conflict. In fact, the potential for *conflict* exists in any situation or event *that involves you and someone else* in your SOS system. This is so because each person's experience — sensory data, thoughts, emotions, wants, and actions — in the situation is different and unique. As a result, conflict can have its root in any zone of the Awareness Wheel. You and the other(s) can each hold:

■ Differing perceptions of *sensory data*

■ Opposing *beliefs, interpretations, expectations, values*

■ Disturbing *emotions*

■ Competing *wants and interests*

■ Offending *actions*

Recall from Chapter 1 that how you talk and listen to another person (whether in conflict or not) falls into a particular Style of Communication. Also, recall that use of particular styles lead you down the low road — the path many people take in a conflict. On the other hand, use of the talking and listening skills allow you to follow the high road. This chapter describes the way the various styles play out in a conversation when a conflict is present.

Keep in mind that one person in an interaction (and that person could be you) can influence in a positive way the direction the conflict takes.

THE THIRD FORCE IN CONFLICT

Remember from Chapter 2 that three forces are present during a conversation about an issue. When the issue develops into a conflict with someone, the third force of process (how you and the others deal with the conflict) is particularly significant. This is so, because to a large extent, the process determines the amount and quality of the content shared and the type of outcome achieved. Beyond these things, process influences everyone's satisfaction with what happens.

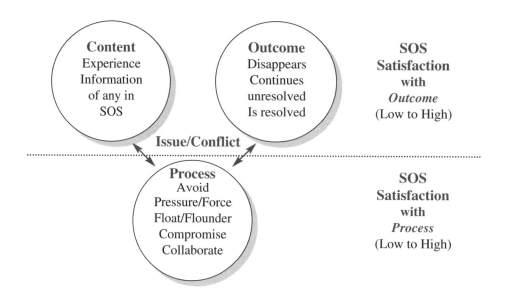

CONTENT

The content is what each person experiences about the issue/conflict — the information related to it. You can:

■ Be aware or not of your own and the other's experience(s).

OUTCOME

Three types of outcomes are possible for a conflict. Basically, it can:

Disappear

■ The issue goes away by itself as time passes.

Continue Unresolved

You and other people involved get stuck and take no action. This may include that you:

■ Live with indecision.

- Agree to disagree longer term.
- Reach a polarized standoff (impasse).

Be Resolved

- You take action that brings the issue to closure.
- You reach a solution.

PROCESS

How you deal with a conflict — your process — has particular importance for several reasons. (Once a conflict arises, regardless of *content*, it moves by *process* toward an *outcome.*) Reasons to pay attention to *process* include:

- *Process* brings out or suppresses the richness of *content*.
- Certain *processes* create better *outcomes* more frequently.
- Improving your *process* increases the likelihood of you and others being more satisfied with both the outcome and the process itself.

Common processes used for interpersonal conflict include:

- Avoid
- Pressure or Force (aggressively or passively)
- Float or Flounder
- Compromise
- Collaborate

The following pages show and describe these processes in relation to the various Styles of Communication.

Satisfaction

You can realize that your satisfaction can range from low to high about the outcomes you reach for your conflicts, as well as about the process you use in dealing with them. Actually, your satisfaction about each of these two aspects can differ. It could be, for example, that you are *satisfied* with the outcome of a conflict for everyone in the SOS System, but *dissatisfied* with the way it all came about — the process.

STYLE YIELDS PROCESS

The graphic below shows how the Styles of Communication relate to the process you use during a conflict.

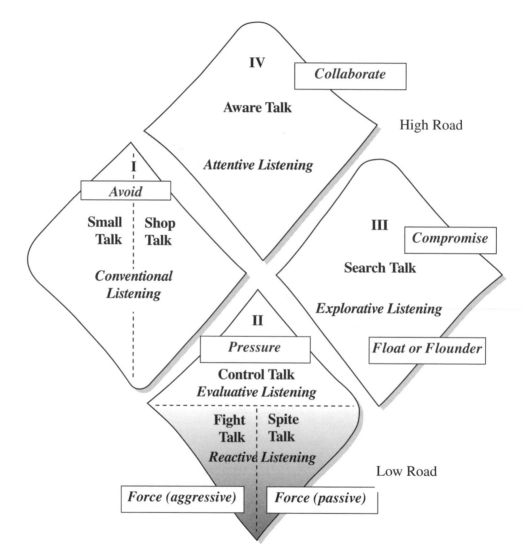

The following pages describe the processes and give their typical impacts on the outcome of the conflicts, as well as on the most likely level of satisfaction for the people involved.

CONFLICT PROCESSES

AVOID

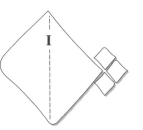

With this process, when an issue comes up that has potential for bringing a conflict with someone, you back off or *flee* from addressing it by using Style I Communication — Small Talk, Shop Talk, or Conventional Listening — to:

- Smooth it over with chit chat, talk about tasks, or joke about it.

- Change the subject.

- Ignore it or deny its existence or significance.

- Skirt around it or refuse to discuss it.

- Claim to be too busy to talk about it.

Typical Impacts of Avoiding the Conflict:

- The outcome happens by chance or default.

- Decisions, problems, and conflicts that may be important to your well-being go unaddressed.

- You and others in the SOS system who have something at stake in the situation are usually dissatisfied.

Other Considerations

- Issues may disappear frequently enough for you to think that avoidance is a useful strategy.

- Sometimes avoiding an issue is acceptable — unless avoidance is your only or main approach for handling conflict. (A good rule of thumb is to pick, prioritize and process the critical issues.)

PRESSURE OR FORCE

During a conflict, by using this process with a form of Style II Communication, you apply pressure or force (either aggressively or passively), attempting to get your way.

Pressure

The approach with *pressure* uses Control Talk and Reactive Listening to:

- Push for agreement, especially on a particular course of action.
- Suppress someone else's point of view — discounting parts of his or her Wheel.

Typical Impacts of Pressure During Conflict:

- Pre-closure often occurs, bringing uninformed decisions.
- The "expedience-efficiency" generates "false agreements."
- Your decisions become unilateral.
- Satisfaction among those in the SOS relationship system suffers.

Aggressive Force

If you do not gain compliance, and tension still exists, you drop further on the low-road by applying *aggressive force* with Fight Talk to:

- Make your argument stronger.
- Intimidate for power, being abrasive.

Typical Impacts of Aggressive Force During Conflict:

- Negative emotions rule for you and the others.
- The struggle for control saps energy.
- Often you and the others lock up in a rigid impasse — fragmented and polarized.
- Relationships suffer damage and may take time to repair.
- Usually no one is satisfied when it is over.

Passive Force

With this process during a conflict, you use Spite Talk as a *passive force* to get your way. Approaches include to:

- Deceive or mislead others or exaggerate about what is really true (*falsify* information).

- Make undercutting and incongruent remarks.

- Divert attention from the issue or blur it with another one.

- Appear to give in to the other, yet continue to harm the other(s) in non-direct ways.

Typcial Impacts of Passive Forcing During Conflict:

- Trouble continues to smolder under the surface.

- Resentment and distrust thrive. (Others still experience the negativity from the non-direct behaviors.)

- Relationships cool or are damaged.

FLOAT OR FLOUNDER

In a conflict, the use of Style III Communication with Search Talk and Explorative Listening can make a good transition for reaching the high-road to find a solution that is mutually satisfactory to the people involved. These styles can give a helpful direction to the conversation when they lead to more depth (with Style IV).

However, when applied alone in a conflict (without that move to Style IV), these styles often wind up getting you nowhere. This means you simply float or actually flounder around the conflict, often with disappointing outcomes.

Float

With this process, you float about, staying in Search Talk and Explorative Listening to:

- Look for solutions but go around the issue so you never find answers.

- Speculate about causes and pose unrealistic possibilities.

- Skim the surface of an issue, leaving out critical parts (for example, emotions or wants).
- Ask safe or irrelevant questions.
- Fail to question unclear or incongruent points.
- Do not commit to take congruent action.

Typical Impacts of Floating During Conflict:

- Nothing is resolved — nothing changes. You and others involved are left hanging.
- Even when issues appear to be treated seriously, no follow-through occurs.
- Inaction is frustrating and dissatisfying. It can dampen relationships.

Flounder

With this process, your communication is not purposeful or on target for the conflict at hand. You stay in Style III to:

- Make excuses for past ineffective action.
- Make inappropriate remarks or get off the subject.
- Do not intend to get involved or treat the conflict seriously enough to take action.
- Ask inappropriate questions.
- Operate according to the 20/80 Rule rather than the 80/20 Rule (see page 46 in Chapter 2), meaning you look to someone or something outside the situation to resolve the conflict.

Typical Impacts of Floundering During Conflict

- Issues are mishandled.
- Time is wasted.
- Indecision and lack of commitment breed discouragement and cynicism.

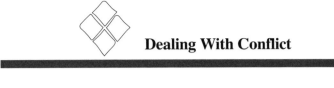

COMPROMISE

With this process, you primarily use Search Talk and Explorative Listening to discover and arrange a solution through trade-offs with others. *Compromise* typically falls somewhere between Styles III and IV as you express your wants for yourself (through Aware Talk) and draw the other(s) out (through Attentive Listening) to discover their wants. You commit to action and ask them if they are willing to do so, as well. You use the combination of styles to:

■ Figure out and willingly exchange concessions of differing importance to one another.

■ Sometimes operate on partial awareness, rather than on complete information.

■ Give something to get something.

Typical Impacts of Compromising During Conflict:

■ Each person gains and loses something.

■ Often you (and the others, too) tend to remember what you gave up (lost) more than what you gained (won).

■ Your resolutions are conditional or even fragile and can become an unintended set-up for failure. That is, if one of you does not keep your part of the bargain, the other one receives license to break the agreement, as well.

■ In the end, compromise is not usually very satisfactory to the people involved.

Note:

Compromise is often the highest level of resolution most people can achieve, because it takes additional knowledge, skill, and goodwill (caring) on the part of both yourself and others to reach a higher level.

COLLABORATE

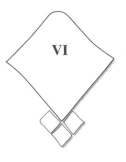

This process goes beyond compromise. With *collaboration*, you use Aware Talk and Attentive Listening to:

- Disclose critical information (your full Awareness Wheel).

- Listen to understand and comprehend.

- Converse without attacking or defending.

- Allow differences to be expressed and not suppressed.

- Incorporate, to the extent possible, the interests of those involved — counting everyone in your SOS network.

- Generate or invent best-fit solutions by including SOS input.

- Commit to follow through with congruent action.

Typical Impacts of Collaborating During Conflict:

- Each person in the conversation is given voice.

- Solutions are reached that no one person could have created by himself or herself.

- Agreements and solutions are built on understanding.

- More time is necessary to work through the process, because it seeks full information and understanding.

- In the long run, you save time and energy (from the fall-out that results from poor or partial decision-making).

- Both the process and the outcome yield the highest possible levels of satisfaction for everyone in your SOS system.

CONFLICT PATTERNS

As you have learned about the various processes for dealing with conflicts, you no doubt have found that one or another of them resonates with you, as far as what you do in conflict. Plus, the type of outcome you generally reach may be familiar to you, as well. Actually, if you tend to experience the same process and note that the outcomes share a similarity, you recognize your pattern. You perhaps see that:

- A process and an outcome combine to develop a conflict pattern.

- The combination of process and outcome usually produces a certain level of satisfaction (or dissatisfaction).

For instance maybe you avoid issues, and eventually they go away, but you experience a low level of satisfaction at leaving things to chance. Or perhaps you try to force others and often wind up reaching standoffs with them. Upon reflection, you find this to be unsatisfying, too.

It is possible to have a couple of patterns for handling issues. For example, you may use:

- A particular pattern for handling disagreements in your family.

- A different pattern for dealing with conflicts involving other people.

Points to Consider

- Recognizing your typical pattern(s) for dealing with conflict is a foundational step for making a change if you desire to do so.

- Understanding the styles and knowing the skills give you choices in how you process issues and conflicts.

- Consciously shifting your Style of Communication will change your process for dealing with an issue or conflict. Applying the skills can take you to the high road as you work out a process, and this will likely bring you more satisfaction as you resolve your conflicts.

MY PATTERNS OF CONFLICT RESOLUTION

Below is the list of processes and outcomes that make up patterns of conflict resolution. (This is regardless of the particular content.) Satisfaction (with levels from low to high) can be felt for the process itself and for the outcome or the conflict.

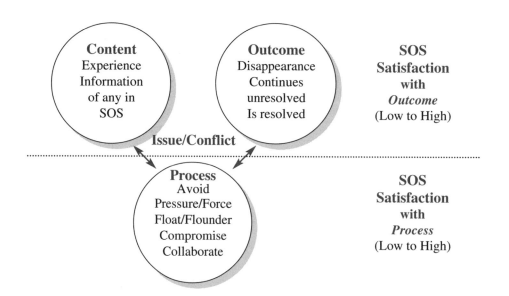

Instructions

Think about two conflicts that have been significant for you. Choose a conflict with:

    1. Someone in your family.

    2. Someone else.

For each, reflect on and then write (on the next page) what the conflict was about, (in just a word or two to identify it), the process you used, the outcome, and the level of satisfaction for you and the others in your SOS network:

Exercise

Use the space below to reflect upon and recall what happened:

> For satisfaction, place arrows ↑ up, ↓ down, or ↑↓ mixed (up and down) for Self (S), Others (O) directly involved, and for the Stakeholders (S).

1. With a family member:

Issue/Conflict	Process	Outcome	SOS Satisfaction (Low, Medium, High)	
			Process	Outcome
			S O S	S O S

2. With someone else:

Issue/Conflict	Process	Outcome	SOS Satisfaction (Low, Medium, High)	
			Process	Outcome
			S O S	S O S

How were these two conflict situations similar or different?

Notes

7

THE SKILLSZONE MAP

Inside and Out
What Takes You Out
Managing Yourself — 5 Guidelines

In a conversation that is important to you, you stand figuratively (or literally using the skills mats) with the six talking and five listening skills before you. This means you can apply the skills in any sequence and combination, at any appropriate time or place, in the discussion. When you engage another person by using skills, you can think of yourself as communicating in the "SkillsZone."

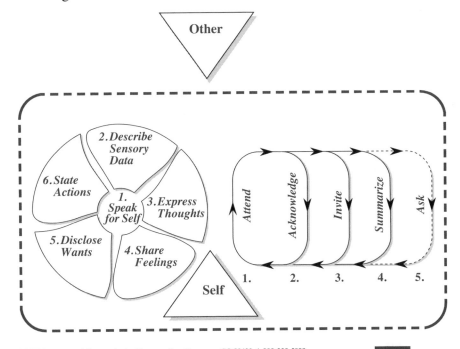

Regardless of the Other Person . . .

Your use of the skills does not depend on other people also applying them. Rather, you can bring your awareness and employ the skills, in a caring way, to influence others positively through your behavior.

Certainly it is easier to stay skilled when the other person is doing so, as well. Yet, this may not always be the case. You could be in a serious conversation with someone who has never learned communication skills in the first place. Then, when an issue arises, it is up to you to stay in the SkillsZone. Recall from the Introduction the assumption that it takes just one person to influence an interaction positively. By yourself, you can make a difference.

INSIDE THE SKILLSZONE

When you are in the SkillsZone, you use:

- Style IV talking (Aware) and listening (Attentive) plus Style III talking (Search) and listening (Explorative) to *focus* on an issue. You *flow* between your talking and listening.

OUTSIDE THE SKILLSZONE

Consider how you operate when you leave this zone of skills during a discussion of an important issue. Possibilities include that you:

- Press forward, going out of the skilled area, by using Style II talking (Control or Fight) or listening (Evaluative or Reactive) to *force* the issue. This is really an attempt to intimidate the other.

- Retreat backwards, away from the skilled area, by using Style I talking (Small or Shop), inappropriate for the situation, or listening (Conventional) to *flee* from the issue. You may even *freeze* in silence with no talk at all. You are intimidated by the issue or the other person.

- Move off to the left side, by using a deceptive form of Style II talking (Spite), misrepresenting, hiding, or mocking information, to *falsify* the issue.

- Slide out the other side, by getting off track and irrelevant with Styles III talking (Search) or Style I listening (Associational) to *float* away from or around the issue. (This is *not* the same as using Search Talk of Style III appropriately to help you approach and explore the issue.) You wind up *floundering* about the issue.

The diagram on the next page shows what happens by staying inside or leaving the SkillsZone during an important discussion.

INSIDE AND OUTSIDE THE SKILLSZONE

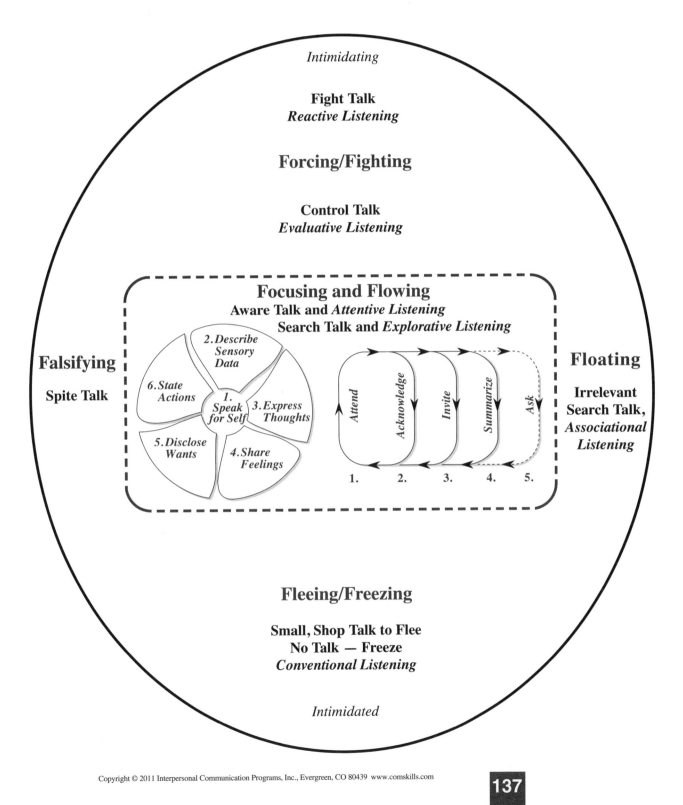

Intimidating

Fight Talk
Reactive Listening

Forcing/Fighting

Control Talk
Evaluative Listening

Focusing and Flowing
Aware Talk and *Attentive Listening*
Search Talk and *Explorative Listening*

Falsifying

Spite Talk

2. *Describe Sensory Data*
6. *State Actions*
1. *Speak for Self*
3. *Express Thoughts*
5. *Disclose Wants*
4. *Share Feelings*

Attend
Acknowledge
Invite
Summarize
Ask

1. 2. 3. 4. 5.

Floating

Irrelevant Search Talk,
Associational Listening

Fleeing/Freezing

**Small, Shop Talk to Flee
No Talk — Freeze**
Conventional Listening

Intimidated

WHAT TAKES YOU OUT OF THE SKILLSZONE?

When anxiety or fear — that you experience as pressure and stress — arises as the demands on you (immediate or cumulative) exceed your available resources to handle the situation(s), you can easily leave the SkillsZone. *Unmanaged anxiety and fear, together with lack of skill, take you outside of the SkillsZone.* How does this happen?

An "Alarm" Goes Off in Sensory Data

The alarm stems from what you:

- See or hear — *external sources.*

- Imagine, visualize, or recall — *internal sources.*

The sources may be:

- A person — someone with whom you find it difficult to deal.

- Information — threatening words, nonverbals, or disappointing news.

- An event — important conversation, a deadline, or potential conflict.

- A pattern — repeated misbehavior or broken promises.

- An object — malfunctioning equipment or software.

- Tasks — too numerous or complicated, unclear or conflicting in priority.

Influential Thoughts Enter

Your evaluation of the resources available for dealing with the alarm determines, to a large extent, your capacity to handle the situation. Resources may be:

- *Personal resources* such as your knowledge, skills, and experience — your belief about your competence, and confidence.

- *Support resources* such as your access to time, finances, others' expertise or backing.

Other thoughts may be about potential danger or negative consequences.

Powerful Emotions Arise

Regardless of the alarm, when you recognize that you may not have the resources to meet the demands of the situation, *mild anxiety to outright fear arises.* Sometimes you feel deep disappointment or possibly anger. As a result, your muscles immediately tighten (particularly in your upper body), registering and broadcasting tension and stress.

Immediate Wants Kick In

These can be to survive, defend yourself, control or fix the situation, or win the argument.

HOW YOU LEAVE THE SKILLSZONE

Sensory Data

An "alarm" goes off, externally or internally

Current

Actions Past

Future

Thoughts

Fight
Flee
Falsify
Flounder

Issue Situation

• Demand exceeds ability/ resources
• Potential threat/danger
• Negative consequences

Desire to:
Survive
Defend
Control
Fix
Win

Self

Other(s) Wants for:

Stakeholder(s)

Annoyance, Anger

Anxiety
Fear
Disappointment

Emotions

You Choose an Action

Under pressure, a tendency exists to rely on familiar, somewhat comfortable, best-of-your-ability, available, and expedient default responses. These low-road urges are "wired" physically into your brain and nervous system, and they take you outside the SkillsZone. As anxiety increases in yourself (and possibly in the others involved), the natural choices are to:

- *Flee* from the situation or *freeze* in place.
- *Force* what happens to take external control of the situation.
- *Falsify* to cover for yourself.
- *Float* to distract or *flounder* to grab at anything.

WAYS TO OPERATE OUTSIDE THE SKILLS ZONE

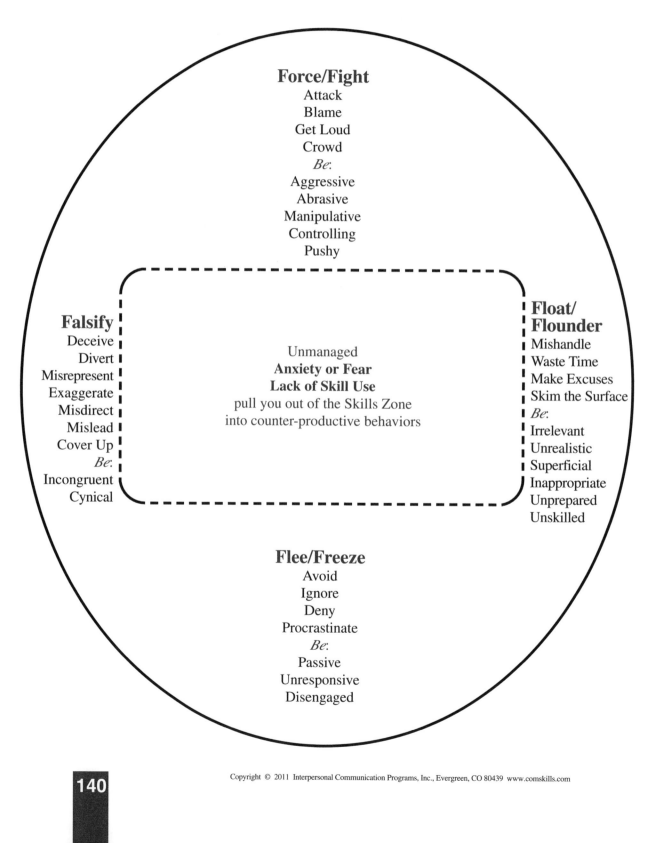

Force/Fight
Attack
Blame
Get Loud
Crowd
Be:
Aggressive
Abrasive
Manipulative
Controlling
Pushy

Falsify
Deceive
Divert
Misrepresent
Exaggerate
Misdirect
Mislead
Cover Up
Be:
Incongruent
Cynical

Unmanaged
Anxiety or Fear
Lack of Skill Use
pull you out of the Skills Zone
into counter-productive behaviors

**Float/
Flounder**
Mishandle
Waste Time
Make Excuses
Skim the Surface
Be:
Irrelevant
Unrealistic
Superficial
Inappropriate
Unprepared
Unskilled

Flee/Freeze
Avoid
Ignore
Deny
Procrastinate
Be:
Passive
Unresponsive
Disengaged

 **Exercise**

HOW I OPERATE OUTSIDE THE SKILLS ZONE

Instructions: Think of challenging situations — with people, events, objects, or tasks — where you experience some degree of anxiety and go outside the SkillsZone.

1. Draw circles of varying sizes to represent the frequency and direction you go.

2. In the circles, list your reasons (thinking) for going outside, and list your typical counter-productive behaviors (actions) outside the Skills Zone.

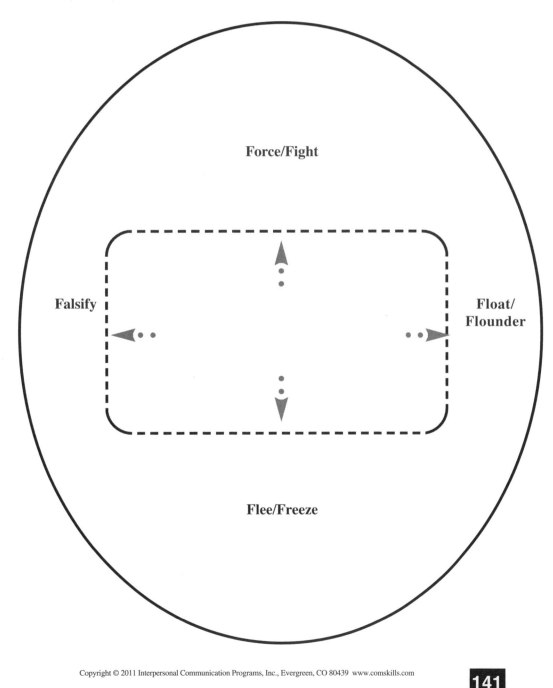

MANAGING YOURSELF — The Key to Communicating Effectively in the SkillsZone

Interacting skillfully in situations of pressure and stress tests your effectiveness as a communicator more than anything else. Consider these points:

■ Research on stress indicates that the way a person responds to and deals with pressure is much more important to his or her well-being than any particular source of the stress itself.

■ Although you are not always able to control when, where, and how issues arise, you can control how you respond to them.

Taking steps to manage yourself and connect with others effectively when you experience pressure and conflict gives you the means to enrich your personal life, as well as to increase your professional competence.

FIVE INTERACTIVE GUIDELINES — For Getting Into, Staying In, and Returning to the SkillsZone

As you enter the SkillsZone and engage in a conversation with someone, especially with a person who has differing sensory data, opinions (thoughts), emotions, or wants, it is helpful to apply several interactive guidelines. These keep you focused and flowing, and they can prevent you from leaving the SkillsZone or help you get back in if you slip out of it. They build on guidelines introduced in Chapter 4 ("Establishing and Maintaining Rapport" and "Watching the Hot and Cold Nonverbals"), with the hot and cold emphasized again in Chapter 5 with the listening skills.

The guidelines in this chapter include actions for connecting with yourself and for connecting with others:

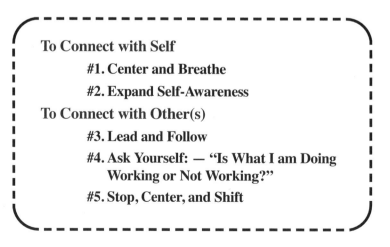

To Connect with Self

    #1. Center and Breathe

    #2. Expand Self-Awareness

To Connect with Other(s)

    #3. Lead and Follow

    #4. Ask Yourself: — "Is What I am Doing Working or Not Working?"

    #5. Stop, Center, and Shift

The next few pages describe these guidelines.

TO CONNECT WITH SELF — in the Skills Zone

The first two guidelines are your own personal foundations for connecting effectively with someone else in a stressful exchange.

Guideline #1: Center and Breathe — A Basis for Managing Self

As soon as you experience an external or internal alarm, *center and breathe,* consciously and immediately. This is like clicking the refresh button on your computer. Doing the process relaxes and rebalances the muscles throughout your body that have tightened with the alarm. This is an essential step in managing yourself as you encounter stressful situations.

Centering may seem counter-intuitive, yet the effect is that of readying you to take the high road. Being centered:

- Supports expanded self-awareness (using your Awareness Wheel) and creates a physical readiness and availability for attentive listening.

- Allows you to access the talking and listening skills more easily.

- Gives you increased physical strength, flexibility, and energy.

- Prepares you to respond to stressors more effectively.

- Produces an unconscious calming, relaxing effect on the others.

Your physical center is just below the middle of your abdomen, a natural balanced midpoint from which you can exert minimum effort for maximum results. This axletree is located about one-and-a-half to two inches below your navel and inside your body, from the front, one-third of the way back toward your backbone. The muscular-skeletal structure and energy necessary to sit, stand, move, and manage yourself in an interaction is optimally balanced above and below this midpoint.

When you are at center, you are in an alert yet relaxed state. Your muscles throughout your body do not work against themselves, causing inefficiency and fatigue. Rather, from your physical power center, you can do your best at many things, such as playing a sport or relating to another person.

How to Go to Center (and Rebalance)

At first, the easiest way to go to center is to:

1. Take a deep, relaxing breath through your nose, with your mouth closed. (You will be breathing diaphragmatically.)

2. Use your hand, as you breathe, to press gently into your stomach at the point about one-and-a-half to two inches below your navel to help you recognize and experience your center.

3. Notice your body relax, calm, and settle (rebalance) itself naturally around your mid-section. This releases accumulated tension in your upper body and reconfigures your nonverbal presence.

Breathing diaphragmatically helps you center. However, with practice, you can go to center without taking a breath, simply by letting your muscles relax instantly around your midpoint.

Points to Consider

■   You can center yourself while sitting, standing, walking, or lying down.

■   Other people read your stress cues (or lack of them) in an interaction. You can calm others by calming yourself.

■   On average, the human brain weighs about two percent of total body weight, but consumes about twenty percent of the oxygen a person inhales. Oxygen is the brain's major nutrient. Centering and breathing in stressful situations increases oxygen to the brain when it is most needed — to think clearly and creatively.

■   Centering and breathing can facilitate your own comfortable, non-anxious silence when that is appropriate during an exchange.

■   When centered, you are relaxation-in-motion, relating from your power center without trying to be powerful. Your nonverbals reflect your presence — radiating dynamic, relaxed strength, rather than static tension and stress. Managing yourself helps you to influence the situation positively.

> To manage your own anxiety and pressure, and
> to help others to calm theirs: Go to Center.

Guideline #2: Expand Your Awareness

In a stressful situation, the Awareness Wheel can help you connect with your own experience — with what is going on with you at this point in time. Ask yourself, "What is happening right now?" Apply self-talk to reflect on parts of your Wheel.

Any part of your Awareness Wheel can generate an issue.

- Sensory Data — unexpected information
- Thoughts — negative beliefs, interpretations
- Emotions — frustration or disappointment
- Wants — blocked desires or wishes
- Actions — ineffective behavior

If you anticipate a conversation that may be difficult, in preparation, use your pad with a Wheel on it to write out, expand, and clarify your awareness. Then, as you internalize the tool, you can use it anywhere, anytime to understand yourself (and others) better, faster, on the spot.

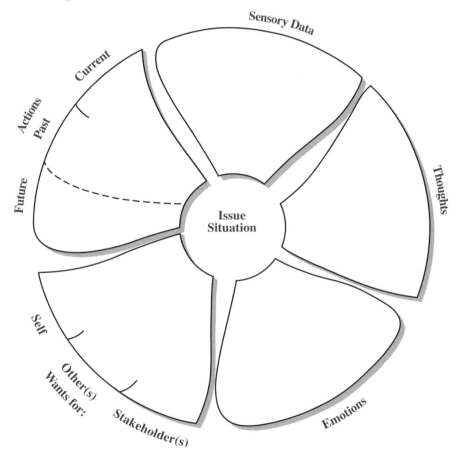

CONNECT WITH OTHER(S) — From Inside the SkillsZone

The ability to engage with someone in an important conversation where you face stress and difference calls on (in addition to self-management and self-awareness) your awareness of others and use of skills. The next three guidelines combine these in a practical way.

Guideline #3: Lead and Follow

Besides considering the skills as talking and listening skills, another way to think of them is to view them as engaging behaviors for *leading* or *following* the interaction.

- Leading means talking or asking questions. When you lead, you attempt to direct where the conversation goes.

- Following means attentive listening. When you follow, you tune into the other person.

The skills can help you do both more effectively.

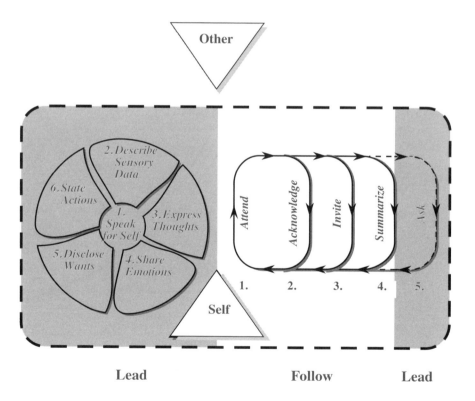

The two shaded areas in the diagram across the page highlight the *leading* behaviors.

■ On the left are the talking skills based on the Awareness Wheel.

■ On the far right is the listening skill of asking open questions — still a leading behavior.

Remember from Chapter 5 that questions come from the asker's agenda (awareness, curiosity, or interest), and not necessarily from that of the one who is telling about the issue or initiating the discussion. Keep in mind:

■ When you ask questions, you are influencing the direction of the conversation.

■ Depending on the situation, asking can be a useful leading behavior, or it can be sidetracking and even distracting.

The clear area in the diagram across the page represents the *following* behaviors.

■ These behaviors are composed of the first four listening skills.

The major purpose of the four listening skills is to allow and encourage the talker to lead in any direction, in order for the listener to discover and understand the talker's experience.

Consider . . .

In a conflicted conversation, most people would rather lead (talk or ask questions) than follow (listen attentively). At the same time, most people also want to be listened to and understood accurately. The ability to manage your own part of the interaction as to when to lead and when to follow will bring rewards in your relationships and will increase your personal influence.

Before continuing to the next guideline, consider the conclusions on the next page about these two processes.

CONCLUSIONS ABOUT LEADING AND FOLLOWING

The Leading Process

When you lead, you:

- Reach out to initiate conversation.
- Direct the conversation.
- Give voice to your own experience.
- Enable others to understand your perspective.
- Help reach resolution.

Hesitations About Leading

You may hesitate to lead to avoid:

- Initiating change.
- Making a commitment.
- Taking responsibility, being accountable.
- Offending someone.
- Saying something that can be seen as foolish or that can be criticized.
- Over-disclosing.

The Following Processs

When you follow, you:

- Gain the other's perspective.
- Expand information from the other person.
- Maintain and display self-control
- Show the other you value his or her input.
- Develop a basis for collaboration.

Hesitations About Following

You may hesitate to follow to avoid:

- Losing control of the situation.
- Being mistaken as agreeing.
- Showing weakness.
- Hearing about something you do not want to recognize or handle.
- Being boxed in.

With communication skill and an attitude of caring for yourself and others in your SOS network, you can take steps to overcome your hesitations for leading or following. The next guidelines will help you develop further your abilities to apply these processes wisely.

Guideline #4: Ask Yourself: "Is What I Am Doing "Working or Not Working?"

When you are in a serious discussion with another person, if what you are doing in the exchange seems to be *working* — meaning you are connecting and things are going well — you probably feel pleased. If, on the other hand, you realize (perhaps in a split second) that what you are doing is *not working* — meaning that you are meeting resistance (disagreement) or not being heard — you may feel dissatisfied or frustrated. No doubt you want something else to be happening.

How do you judge if your conversation is working or not working in any situation?

Hot or Cold Nonverbals

One way to evaluate, besides hearing the words, is to watch others' hot or cold responses. Recall from Chapter 4 that people show the positive (hot) or negative (cold) effect you are having upon them through their nonverbals. These subtle or not so subtle behaviors include, for example:

■ Visual — small facial changes, gestures, head movements and posture shifts.

■ Voice — rate, pitch, volume, and tone.

Some nonverbals consist of even larger bodily gestures.

Since nonverbals are spontaneous and hard to control consciously, they provide sensory data as a form of feeback that you might not gain from the words alone. So the next time you are in an important exchange, pay attention to the other person's hot or cold nonverbals (in addition to their words) to determine if your leading or following behavior is working or not working.

Choice Point — Potential Turning Point

If what you are doing in the conversation is not working, you are at a choice point — a potential turning point in the interaction.

Think about what you usually do in an exchange (especially about an issue) when it is not working. Most people continue doing the same thing, but do so harder, faster, or louder, while expecting the other person to change. This often unwittingly perpetuates the same unsatisfactory response.

Instead of continuing something that is ineffective, apply the next guideline.

Guideline #5: Recognize (that what you are doing is not working) — Stop, Center, and Shift.

In a conversation that is not going well, *recognize* what is going on, and *stop, center, and shift* to another behavior. For example:

- If you are leading (talking or questioning), stop, center, and shift to following (listening, such as inviting the other to talk).

- If you are following (acknowledging, for instance), stop, center, and shift to leading (such as disclosing your wants for the other person).

Watch the hot and cold nonverbal and the verbal response of the other person(s). Notice if your shift improves the interactive process. If so, your action has created a positive turning point. If it does not, make another shift.

When what you are doing is not working, you have probably moved off center, out of balance. This is a clue to center, breathe, and rebalance.

Other Stop, Center, and Shifts

Ways to stop, center, and shift (besides changing from leading to following and vice versa) include:

- Altering zones of the Awareness Wheel (for example, go from focusing on your emotions to giving your past behavior that has contributed to the situation).

- Changing the skill in the Listening Cycle (for example, go from attending to the other's talk to summarizing the experience, and then checking to see if your summary is accurate).

- Switching to another Style of Communication (for example, move to Search Talk, saying, for instance, that perhaps it was your past inattentiveness that let things go so far). Then be sure to move back to Style IV (for example, by saying that you want to make things work for all involved).

- Changing posture (for example, move from sitting to standing or from standing to sitting).

- Opening or closing space — move closer or farther away — the opposite of what you have been doing.

- Lowering or slowing down your voice.

When you recognize that things are not flowing smoothly in an interaction with another person, stop and shift your own behavior, with the purpose of connecting better with him or her.

Experiment in a conversation. Do not keep doing what is not working. You can apply this recognize-stop-and-shift guideline to brief interactions as well as to life patterns that are not working.

INTERACTIVE COROLLARIES

- As long as you keep doing what you are doing, you will keep getting what you are getting.

  If you want something different, you must do something different.

- If you change, a high probability exists that the other person will respond differently (hopefully favorably) to your change.

- If your use of a particular skill appears to disrupt the conversation or to annoy the other person, do not use the skill in that situation. (Nothing works all the time.)

  Since it takes one person to change an interaction (an assumption in CORE COMMUNICATION), you can decide if that one person is you.

The Key:

Recognize when something is not working, and stop, center, and shift. Positively changing one part of your behavior will align other aspects as well.

It is important to find your own comfortable natural way to use the skills. Self-awareness helps you recognize how you are acting and responding. By managing yourself — controlling your own contributions and responses — you are also better able to connect with others and deal with the situation.

Principle: Interconnections

You may ask yourself, "How can I remember all these guidelines?" You do not need to remember them all: They interconnect. For example, when you change your communication style from Fight Talk to Aware Talk, you also change your breathing. Likewise, when you center and breathe, you reduce your tension. Typically, this shifts you into a more open communication style.

Successful application of the guidelines requires, in addition to your communication abilities, that you be fully present in the situation and mindful of your behavior, with an attitude of caring toward all involved.

> When you are in the Skills Zone,
> you tend to draw others in as well.

LEADING AND FOLLOWING — NEGOTIATING CHANGE

This exercise gives you an opportunity to experiment during a conversation, using all the skills and interactive guidelines to stay in the SkillsZone. The purpose is to see what you can learn about process and yourself. The exercise involves use of the large floor skills mats.

Instructions for You

1. Think of a conversation about an issue or situation with another person that you would be willing to simulate as a rehearsal or re-run. (You may also consider rehearsing the "Someone I Want to Influence" conversation, from the exercise on page xi in the Introduction and Chapter 3, page 76.)

2. Position the skill mats in the exact configuration illustrated in the graphic below.

3. Select someone to play the role of the surrogate other (to be the person with whom you will converse). Also choose observer-coaches. (See the next page for instructions for the surrogate and the coaches.)

4. Brief the surrogate and observer-coaches with enough background information about the real situation so the surrogate can accurately play the other person in the situation. (During the course of the exercise, coach the surrogate on how to play his or her role, if he or she needs help representing the real person.)

5. As you interact, see if you can "stay in the SkillsZone" — centered, aware, counting self and other, and engaging with skill — without slipping out of the Zone.

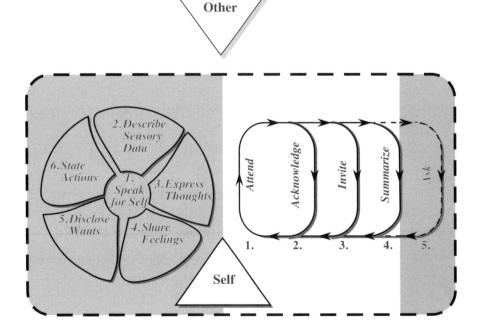

Instructions for Other — the Surrogate

1. Make sure you have enough information (from the person doing the simulation or rehearsal) to be able to play the surrogate with relative accuracy and comfort.

2. As you play the role of the surrogate, respond to the person's behavior as you experience him or her in the interaction. If what he or she is doing is not working, signal "Cold." On the other hand, if what he or she is doing is working with you, signal "Warm." (In a simulation like this, it is possible to lock into a role and not respond positively, regardless of how effective the person's communication is.)

3. Let yourself be influenced — hot or cold — by the person's actual behavior. He or she is experimenting with new behaviors.

Instructions for Observer-Coach(es)

1. Confine your coaching and feedback to *process* — the maps, skills, and guidelines. Do not get sidetracked into discussing the *content* or proposing solutions *(outcomes)*.

2. Attend to the Hot and Cold effectiveness of your feedback to the participant you are observing-coaching. Do not flood the participant with too much information.

3. In giving feedback, be sure to point out things the person has done well, besides indicating anything that could have been changed.

HOW DO I GET BACK INTO THE SKILLSZONE?

Instructions: Think of an example of a conversation in which you could find yourself outside the SkillsZone — where you would experience some degree of anxiety or annoyance or anger. What helps you get back into the SkillsZone when you have left it?

From your experience and from guidelines given in this chapter, list (inside the SkillsZone below) several actions that you could take to re-enter and stay in the SkillsZone.

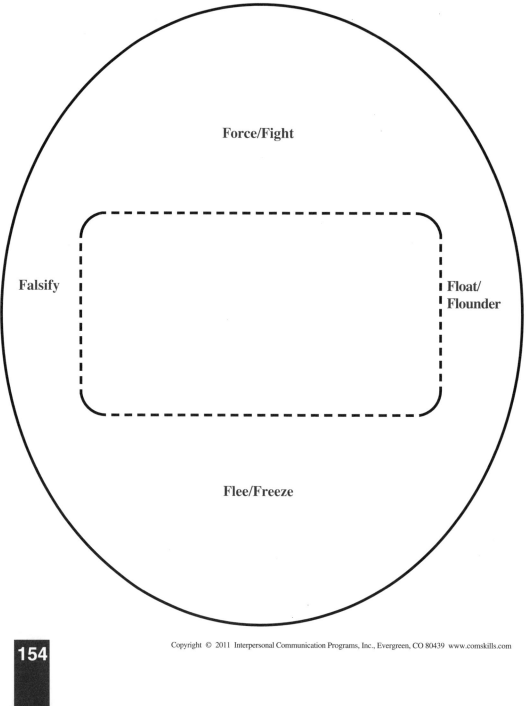

USE YOUR SKILLS LAPTOP MAT

Instructions: If you want to accelerate your learning and benefit from the application of the skills in CORE COMMUNICATION, use your Skills Laptop/Tabletop Mat.

When you set the Skills Lap Mat in front of you, remember that you are constantly making choices — to lead or to follow.

- *Leading* includes using the *six talking skills* (on the Awareness Wheel) and *asking open questions* (on the Listening Cycle).
- *Following* includes the *first four listening skills.*

Several suggestions for making use of the Skills Laptop Mat include:

1. If possible, lay the mat on your lap or a table when you are on the phone. During your phone conversations, "let your fingers do the walking" to:

- Track the process of your conversation.
- Prompt your use of both talking and listening skills.

2. When you are thinking through a serious issue with another person, ask him or her if you could set your Skills Laptop/Tabletop Mat out on the table to help focus and facilitate the conversation.

3. At any time:

- Use the mat to remind yourself of your choices and to expand your options.
- Notice your typical patterns. (What do you usually do?)
- Experiment with different skill combinations.

INSIDE THE SKILLS ZONE — A SUMMARY OF THE DYNAMICS

When you are discussing an issue, a psychological and behavioral "space" exists in which you can be most effective. *Internally* it consists of being aware as you process the issue, and *externally* it means being fully involved in the conversation. *This "productive space" applies self-control and skilled choices, and it lies between the urge to fight or to flee, either of which is a natural response, or to falsify or to flounder, particularly when you are under pressure.*

SPACE is an acronym for the dynamics at work when you are at your best — managing yourself and connecting with other(s) — while focusing on an issue using skilled communication.

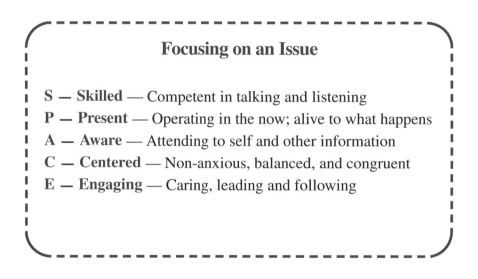

Focusing on an Issue

S — Skilled — Competent in talking and listening
P — Present — Operating in the now; alive to what happens
A — Aware — Attending to self and other information
C — Centered — Non-anxious, balanced, and congruent
E — Engaging — Caring, leading and following

When you use the Talking and Listening Skills to count everyone in your SOS system and focus on an issue, you are operating inside the SkillsZone, communicating in Styles III and IV. In this zone of skilled communication, encompassing all the aspects of the SPACE dynamics, you can engage others in productive conversations more effectively. In challenging situations, it is especially helpful to enter and interact in this zone.

8

SPECIAL PROCESSES

Responding to:
Resistance
Fight Talk
Spite Talk

When someone challenges or attacks you verbally (using Style II communication), what do you do? Assuming you determine not to flee, but rather to stay and engage the person, how do you usually respond? Do you do something that *escalates* the tension or that *deescalates* it?

Once you know the skills, how you respond grows from your intention and attitude in such a situation. If your intention is to *control* the other person and win the attack, you will most likely operate outside the SkillsZone. This may make matters worse and *escalate* the negative behavior. If, on the other hand, your intention is to *connect* with the person, you can engage from inside the SkillsZone and actually *deescalate* the threat.

The level of tension in one of these verbal challenges exists on a continuum. This ranges from mild *resistance,* in opposition to your ideas or interests, to a stronger aggressive verbal *attack* or a passive *disengagement.* When Style II communication is anywhere on the continuum, it holds tremendous pulling power. Any hint from one person of a negative Style II message, in Fight Talk or Spite Talk, often easily pulls the other into a Style II reaction, as well. Style II is very strong. Stronger yet are genuine responses for connecting from within the SkillsZone.

This section offers special processes built on the skills and the interactive guides for staying in the SkillsZone when you face resistance or a direct or indirect attack. Each process includes a sequence of steps.

RESPONDING TO RESISTANCE

Turn Resistance Into a Resource

When you propose something (a form of change) to another person, that person may feel cautious or uncertain about it, perhaps thinking he or she is losing control of the situation. The natural tendency of the person is to become protective, disagreeable, and even defensive. His or her body begins to register its reservation (with cold nonverbal responses) to your suggestion. This is resistance. Its expression includes hesitation, objection, opposition, indifference, or rejection.

A typical counter response to resistance is to talk more (keep leading) and increase the pressure. Doing these things creates even more resistance.

As disturbing as resistance can be when you encounter it, the resistance serves an important function — it slows things down until you and the other person can understand what the change will mean and how it will impact you both. Resistance tells you where you are with that person at that moment. It often signals that you are not taking his or her wants and interests into account.

How to Meet Resistance

When you are leading and get two cold responses in a row, recognize that you are encountering resistance. At that point:

1. **Stop, and shift to following.** Offer no more pressure that nourishes more resistance. Breathe and center. Shift to following, using the Attentive Listening skills, and let the person lead you to his or her reluctance.

2. **Continue to follow** — acknowledge, invite, and summarize — until the point of resistance is understood fully and the person gives you critical information that must be incorporated into what you have proposed.

3. **Watch for any nonverbal cue** (facial expression, alteration in posture or tone — a warm response) in the other person to see if what you are now doing is working.

4. **Begin to lead again and rework** what you propose, to incorporate his or her interest.

This is how you turn resistance into a resource — an impasse into useful information.

Remember:

Do not run from resistance. Engage it; explore it; follow it. Like a reliable road sign, resistance tells you where you must go next. It will lead to what must be resolved in order to move ahead freely. This is how you turn resistance into a resource.

Listening and Agreement

As you follow the other person into his or her world, pursuing understanding, you know that you are not necessarily in agreement. (Remember the distinction between understanding and agreement made in Chapter 5.) However, the other person may not realize this. That person might think you agree as he or she talks (leads).

If you believe the other person is interpreting your following (listening) as meaning you are in agreement:

- You can interject, "Please don't take my listening to mean that I am in agreement. I am just trying to understand fully what you are saying. I'm not necessarily agreeing with it."

- Or you might say, "This is hard for me to hear, but keep going."

Recognizing and freely exploring resistance is the quickest way to remove roadblocks to discover a satisfactory outcome.

Suggestions Related to Resistance:

- Invite resistance to test the fit of something. Ask, for example, "Where are you with this?" or "In what way doesn't this fit for you?" You will move quickly to discover what is blocking things and what needs to be resolved.

- Choice reduces resistance. Allow other choices.

Consider:

- If you ignore the resistance, it will continue and interfere with a best-fit solution.

- If you do not deal with the resistance, you will waste time, and possibly end up with a false agreement or impasse.

- Resistance is a potential connecting point.

EXERCISE: CHANGE WHAT I DO THAT DOES NOT WORK

1. **Think about** what you typically do in a conversation, when you encounter resistance, that does not work. (Write notes or share this with someone.)

2. **Imagine yourself** in such a conversation, but instead of doing what you typically would do, use the tabletop mat or the floor skill mats to rehearse shifting into doing something more productive — engaging the resistance.

3. **Look for your next opportunity** to apply your new behavior.

RESPONDING TO FIGHT TALK

When someone is using Fight Talk, the person is negatively charged, directly and actively challenging or verbally attacking you. Your job is to engage the person (if possible) and rechannel the negative emotion into a productive outcome.

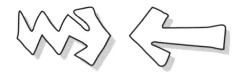

Note: If you think you are in any physical danger, leave the situation. Get out of harm's way. Protect yourself! In any exchange with an angry person, keep a safe physical distance.

If you choose to engage the person, follow the steps below to do so from the SkillsZone:

1. **Recognize the other person's nonverbal pressure cues:** These include upper body and facial tension, forceful gestures, and strident tone of voice. Also notice the angry words.

2. **Breathe and center:** This lets go of your own negative energy (your tension or muscle strain) and positions you for more centered, flexible responses. Let yourself assume an open, alert, non-defensive posture.

3. **Tune into the other's experience:**

   Attend: Look, Listen, and Track.

   Acknowledge the other person's emotion (often unstated feeling of anger, fear, or frustration). Then:

   Invite, encourage the person to continue telling his or her full story.

   Summarize the concerns to demonstrate to the person that he or she has been heard accurately (even if you do not agree with what he or she has said).

4. **If possible, express a want for other** (based on the other's interest.)

This process neutralizes the attacker by going with his or her energy and offering nothing for the challenger to resist.

5. **Watch for warming nonverbals** before you attempt to lead in any way.

6. **Look and listen for real signs of relieved pressure — no Fight Talk.** Pick up on and complete any unfinished concerns. Continue to deal with the issue in a calm way by doing repeated breathing and centering. Stay in the SkillsZone by using Aware Talk and Attentive Listening.

Other Potentially Connecting Responses

When facing Fight Talk, other responses may also be helpful. These include:

- Agreeing with what is being said if you can honestly do so.
- Extending what the person is saying. (For example, "It's worse than what you are saying.")
- Admitting what you have done or what has happened if the person is accurate. (Be accountable.)
- Give genuine credit. (For example, "You're doing me a favor by pointing this out.")
- Joining by sharing (in Aware Talk) your own frustration (not directed at the other) with the situation.

The key to the effectiveness of any of these responses is being congruent about your own experience with them.

Suggestions

- Do not meet a challenger with rational reasons, or tell the person why he or she should not feel that way. You will receive a cold response and escalate the tension.
- Do not move too quickly to leading. Demonstrate understanding and caring before attempting to lead. Do not just say, sincerely or not, "I understand," as a transition to direct the exchange.
- Keep centered. Your relaxed flexible responses will have a calming effect on the other person.

EXERCISE: RESPOND TO FIGHT TALK

1. **Recall a situation** in which someone used Fight Talk with you. If you could re-do the situation, what would you do, using the process above? (Write notes on page 164 or share your steps in the process with someone.)
2. **Watch for** a time or a place in which you can apply this process with someone you know who uses Fight Talk with you.

RESPONDING TO SPITE TALK

When someone is using Spite Talk, the person signals a negative, unhappy undercurrent by withholding or challenging you passively and indirectly. The style reflects someone who is lethargic, disengaged, hurt, or angry. Your job is to connect with the other person in a way that helps energize and focus his or her discontent toward a more constructive resolution.

A. **Recognize the nonverbals** (the other person's pressure cues). For example, notice disengaged posture, flat facial expression, lack of eye contact, sighs, and dull or whiny tone of voice. Also notice the cynical words.

B. **Breathe and center.** This will produce more calmness in the presence of the other person's tense silence and anger. Work from your center and the SkillsZone.

C. **Describe what you see and hear, and ask what is wrong.** Do not let Spite Talk go unacknowledged. Your description may result in:

■ A *positive response* by the person. (Go directly to Steps 5 and 6 on the next page.)

■ A continued *negative response* by the person. (The more passive and powerless the person is, when angry, the more frequently he or she will deny that anything is wrong.)

If you receive a negative response (for instance, you do not get an honest answer):

■ Choose whether or not to pursue the negativity.

　　■ If you choose not to pursue it, let it go.

　　■ If you choose to pursue it, deal with it using the following steps:

　　1. **Break state. Do not keep asking what is wrong.** Do something to get the other to change posture and context, and to breathe. This will physically put him or her in a position to be more responsive. For example, think of an excuse to take a walk together, or get some coffee. Walking or sitting side-by-side also relieves some of the typical face-to-face pressure.

　　2. **Speak for self about the other, demonstrating empathy, if he or she remains silent.** Start by saying that you have been thinking about the other person and describe what you think he or she is experiencing. Try to be as accurate about all parts of his or her situation as you are able to imagine. Also, be willing to own in Aware Talk, if this is congruent for you, anything you have done to contribute to the person getting upset.

3. **Watch for small warming nonverbals** that confirm your accuracy as you speak. (Often the person will either respond positively to your empathy or correct your inaccuracy, if you are inaccurate.) Whatever the response, you have helped energize the person to talk about whatever has wounded him or her. Build on any positive responses.

4. **If you receive no response, do not lapse back into trying to get the other person to talk to you by asking more questions.** Rather, end the conversation by saying, "Take your time to think things over and get back to me when you are ready to talk." (Sometimes hurts acted out in Spite run deep and it takes time for a person to respond.)

If you receive a positive response: For instance, the person says that something is wrong:

5. **Map the issue together.** (Follow the process model of mapping from Chapter 9 of this workbook.)

6. **Offer choices** and act on his or her wants, if possible.

Considerations:

■ Keep in mind that people act with spite when they feel hurt and angry and believe that resentful resistance is the only power they possess.

■ Consider having a conversation (with you staying in the SkillsZone) with the person about his or her pattern of Spite Talk, asking for change in the behavior.

■ Make a decision. When a person continues spiteful behavior after some effort to deal with it on your part, decide to what extent you will continue the relationship and draw boundaries for yourself.

■ If you are in any position of authority over the person, set limits and define consequences, after you have applied the process given above several times. Tell the person that such behavior (be specific and concrete) is unacceptable and must stop or particular consequences will follow. (This would be using Control Talk.)

EXERCISE: RESPOND TO SPITE TALK

1. **Recall a situation** in which someone used Spite Talk with you. If you could re-do the situation, what would you do, using the process above? (Write notes on page 164 or share your steps in the process with someone.)

2. **Anticipate an occasion** for responding to Spite Talk with someone you know who uses this style with you.

Notes for Responding to Fight Talk Exercise:

Notes for Responding to Spite Talk Exercise:

When you encounter negative Style II, reach for the skills.

9

MAPPING AN ISSUE

A Structured Process
For Collaboration

The Mapping-an-Issue process integrates all the talking and listening skills, in Styles III and IV. As a collaborative process, Mapping takes into account all parts of SOS (Self, Other, Stakeholders). The process works for any content, gives best-fit outcomes, and provides the highest possible satisfaction for those involved. By using it, you can guide yourself and others along the high road as you:

- Make a decision
- Solve a problem
- Resolve a conflict.

This process can serve as a guide for navigating your way, as you function in any of these capacities:

- *Colleague/Peer* (with another individual who does not know the skills, and you use the process as a guide for the two of you working out an issue or conflict)
- *Coach/Counselor* (to help another individual who does not know the skills, to find the best way for making a decision or solving a problem)
- *Facilitator/Consultant* (to a group with a situation calling for a collaborative decision or resolution to conflict)

Mapping-an-Issue is particularly helpful when you:

- Think the issue is *important, complicated*, or *controversial.*
- Experience considerable *tension* and *difference of opinion.*
- Want *maximum input* from others about the issue.
- Seek the *best solution* in the situation.
- Are *stuck* or *drifting.*

CHARACTERISTICS OF MAPPING-AN-ISSUE			
Content	**Process**	**Outcome**	**Satisfaction**
Non-Routine	Collaborative All Skills Styles III & IV	Best-Fit	Highest Possible

THE NINE-STEP PROCESS

This process, which takes time and is thorough, provides a structured sequence of applying the talking and listening skills. Its nine steps are:

Step 1. Identify and Define the Issue.

Step 2. Contract to Work Through the Issue.

Step 3. Understand the Issue Completely.

Step 4. Identify Wants for SOS.

Step 5. Generate and Consider Options.

Step 6. Choose "Best Fit" Actions.

Step 7. Test the Action Plan for "Best Fit" and Commitment.

Step 8. Implement Future Action(s).

Step 9. Evaluate the Outcome.

Follow the steps whether you are the colleague/peer, coach/counselor, or facilitator/consultant.

STEP 1. IDENTIFY AND DEFINE THE ISSUE

Your task at this point is to clarify *what* the issue is, and decide *whose* issue it is.

Keep in Mind:

- Issues typically signal a disruption in expectations — a gap between what is *anticipated* and what is actually *experienced,* between what *could be* or *should be* and what *is not.*

- The *cue* to an issue can register in any zone of the Awareness Wheel — sensory data, thoughts, emotion, wants, or action.

- Style II communication signals new or unresolved issues.

Determine:

- *What* is the issue? You may find it helpful to decide the content type:

    Topical — including a task or technical matter

    Personal — individual matter of yourself or of someone else

    Relational — interaction between two people or among several people

    Group — including a family, committee, or team concern

- *Whose* issue is this?

    Self, Other(s), and/or Stakeholder(s)

State the Issue:

- Make sure everyone involved agrees about what the identified issue is.

When you are clear about the issue, proceed to Step 2.

STEP 2. CONTRACT TO WORK THROUGH THE ISSUE — ESTABLISH COMMITMENT AND GROUND RULES

Have you been in a situation with someone when you wanted to talk about an issue, but a productive discussion did not occur? Perhaps it was the wrong time or place, or the other person had no real interest or commitment to resolve the matter. Having a contract can make a big difference in the effectiveness of the conversation that occurs.

Contracting Involves:

- *Establishing everyone's willingness and readiness to work through a particular issue before launching into the conversation.*
- *Setting procedures and ground rules for conducting your discussion before starting it.*

Note:

- Without a good contract — an operational agreement and commitment to work through an issue — any discussion may be hurried, superficial, guarded or incomplete, if it occurs at all.
- The more fast-paced the circumstances are or complex the issue is, the more intentional you must be about contracting, even though the other person(s) do not realize this or think it worth the time or effort.

Elements of a Contract — the Procedural Agreement

Issue	What and Whose? (Step 1)
	Interest/Commitment?
Ground Rules	
Procedures	Who to Include?
	Where to Meet?
	When and for How Long?
How	Talk Openly
	Be Respectful
	Decide About Tools to Use
At Any Point	Call Time Out
	Check Process

To Establish Commitment

Check and confirm the willingness and readiness of those immediately involved to discuss the particular issue before launching into it.

To Set Procedures and Ground Rules:

Determine specific aspects for carrying on the conversation before starting it.

Who, Where, When

Decide in advance:

- *Who* should be, and should not be, included?

    Consider all SOS people. Include key people.

- *Where* will you talk?

    Choose a private place.

    Find a location that fits for everyone.

    Limit distractions.

- *When* will you talk and for how *long*?

    Consider everyone's preferences. Do not force a discussion at the wrong time or you will generate tension and resistance.

    Realize that conversing too long or running out of time before closure are both frustrating and often counterproductive.

How You Will Work

This element sets the tone. Before beginning a discussion, establish operational expectations to:

- Talk openly about the issue.
- Be respectful of one another. (This is counting SOS.)
- Determine aids or tools, For example, decide if it is helpful to have a recorder, post the steps of this model, work at a flip chart, or just sit together. (Keep your pocket card handy for reference, too.)

Determine That Anyone Can:

- *Check Process.* Note that at any time, any participant can briefly "step back" and check each person's satisfaction with the process, its pace, or the productivity of the discussion. To do this, ask questions such as:

  Are we on or off track?

  Are you being understood?

  Should we move ahead (and suggest the next step)?

  Should we stop for now and reschedule?

Contracting itself is a preliminary check-process activity.

- *Call Time Out.* Agree that anyone can call Time Out, for reasons such as:

  Emotions running too high

  Feeling saturated, fatigued

  Wanting to reschedule, or needing more time

Issues do not always need to be resolved at one sitting. Often, time to digest what has been heard or to cool off brings new perspective and resolution. Time Out functions as a safety valve to prevent overheating or information overload.

If Time Out is called, be sure to re-contract to discuss the issue further, when the time is right.

Keep in mind:

- If the parties to an issue are never willing to get together to work out a resolution, the contract itself (and sometimes the future of the relationship) becomes the primary issue.

- It only takes one element of the contract to be out of sync to dampen the process of working through an issue effectively.

- Generally, you will find that establishing ground rules increases each person's involvement.

Suggestions About Contracting

- Running down this list each time you want to deal with an issue is not always necessary. Be aware, however, that some form of an underlying commitment and operating agreement run through every discussion about an issue.

- Notice that when everyone is ready and willing, and the ground rules are set, a surprising amount can be accomplished, even in a limited time frame.

- Attend to participants' nonverbals prior to, as well as during, the discussion for clues about whether or not your contract to work on the issue is in effect. If you are in doubt, check it out.

Sometimes Identifying the Issue and Contracting (Steps 1 and 2) are preliminary and separate from the actual discussion. Other times they immediately precede the discussion.

Contracting ensures that you are getting off to the right start.

> Results rarely exceed the quality of your contract
> — your procedural agreement.

STEP 3. UNDERSTAND THE ISSUE COMPLETELY

The purpose of this step is to *develop complete understanding of the issue before taking action.* This prevents pre-closure — jumping quickly to solutions that do not fit.

To understand the issue, use Open Questions and the Attentive Listening skills to encourage the other(s) involved to talk thoroughly about their experience of the issue. When they have told their story, you use the Talking Skills to contribute your point of view. In effect, you help everyone focus on the four questions (shown in the Awareness Wheel below):

How to Understand the Issue:

■ As each person shares his or her experience with the others, attend to hot and cold responses. Be ready to lead or follow, either as a participant or the facilitator.

■ Keep everyone taking turns — focusing on past/current actions, data, thoughts, and emotions — until everyone has had a chance to share all he or she wishes to say.

■ Sometimes this step takes a while. Remember, however, that understanding is the foundation of effective and congruent future action.

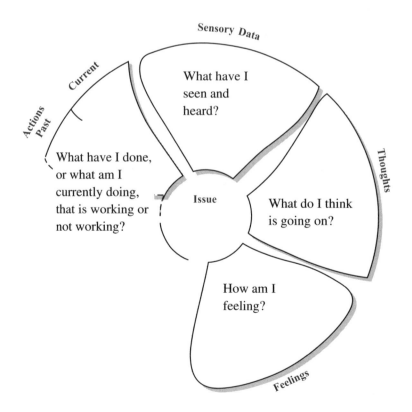

Understanding as the Solution

Occasionally you will discover that it is not necessary to go beyond Step 3, because the very process of understanding the issue in itself has become the solution.

STEP 4. IDENTIFY WANTS

This step focuses on the wants of each person, *for* the SOS System, regarding the issue.

Each needs to determine:

- What do I want *for Self?*
- What do I want *for Other(s)* — the people *centrally* involved?
- What do I want *for* the *Stakeholders* — the people *peripherally* involved yet still affected?

Suggestions:

- Be careful that confusion does not exist between what the participants want *for* others, with what they want *from* others. (Note that what they want *from* others goes under wants *for* self.)
- Recycle everyone's wants for other(s) after you have heard everyone's wants for self. (Sometimes you do not know what you want for others until you have heard them say what they want for themselves.)
- Include *don't wants* as well as *wants.*

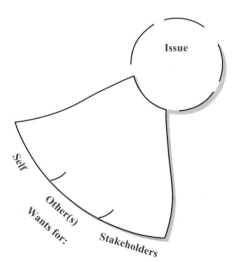

The Key to Collaboration

In resolving conflicts, this step on wants is absolutely critical. To affirm and to build on the wants of others (as well as on one's own wants) is central to success in collaborating.

STEP 5. GENERATE AND CONSIDER OPTIONS

At this point, the people involved in the conversation *brainstorm what they could actually do to resolve the issue,* or at least move it ahead.

First, Generate Options:

- Brainstorm a diverse list of small positive actions that anyone involved can actually take as next steps rather than try to come up with one big solution.

- Keep in view everybody's expanded understanding of the issue (Step 3).

- Take into account wants *for SOS* (Step 4).

- Be sure to include both new possibilities that have not been tried and past actions that have been helpful. (Do not repeat what is not working.)

- Generate possibilities without pausing to critique the options.

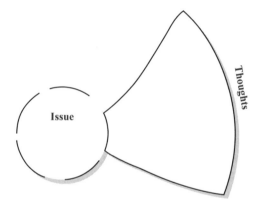

Options:	S	O	S
#1._____	___	___	___
#2._____	___	___	___
#3._____	___	___	___
#4._____	___	___	___
#5._____	___	___	___

Mapping Issues

Next, Consider the Impact (of Each Potential Action on the SOS System):

- Consider the worst and best outcome that could happen with each action.
- Draw an arrow up ↑, down ↓, or up and down — mixed ↑↓ to estimate the fit of each option for every SOS person.

Options:	S	O	S
#1._____	↑	↓	↑↓
#2._____	↓	↑	↑
#3._____	↑	↑	↓
#4._____	↑	↑	↑
#5._____	↑↓	↑	↓

STEP 6. CHOOSE ACTIONS

Choose Best-Fit Action(s) to Implement:

- Choose options that are the most workable and beneficial for the SOS System.
- Synthesize and combine actions if you wish (from Step 5).
- Confirm who will do what by when.

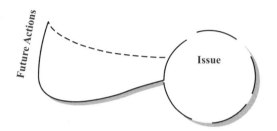

Future Action Plan

Who Will Do What?	By When?
_____	_____
_____	_____
_____	_____
_____	_____

STEP 7. TEST THE ACTION PLAN FOR "BEST FIT" AND COMMITMENT

To test, each person pauses for a moment and imagines self and others who have chosen actions, actually carrying out each of these actions.

■ If each of you sees, hears, and experiences yourself and others following through with each action, great! Your plans fit and commitment exists.

■ If, however, anyone cannot see himself or herself or others carrying out an action, consider where the interference occurs. In this case:

Figure out if any *data, thought, emotion, want,* or *action* exists that does not fit congruently and that dampens the plan? If so, talk about it. Revise the action plan to incorporate the incongruent part.

Determine if the incongruence signals a lack of commitment. If so, revisit action choices.

Consider if the incongruence signals a new issue. If so, decide whether a related or deeper issue is really blocking resolution of the original issue. If time and energy are not available immediately to map and resolve the new issue, contract to deal with the new issue later.

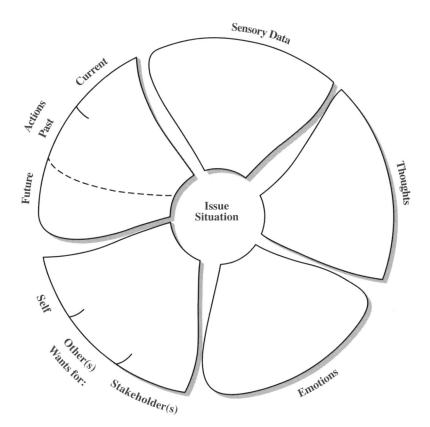

STEP 8. IMPLEMENT FUTURE ACTION(S)

Carry out and follow through with your commitments and promises.

STEP 9. EVALUATE THE OUTCOME

After you have had a chance to act, evaluate your plan and determine how well it worked. (If this issue was one in which you coached or facilitated others, you will need to check with those people about the outcome.)

- If your action has been effective, you will feel pleased. Celebrate!
- If your action has not been effective, you may experience a range of negative feelings — disappointment, frustration, even embarrassment. In this case:

  Determine what you have learned from the experience, and generate a new action plan. (Re-map the issue.)

  Do not keep repeating actions that do not work.

BENEFITS OF MAPPING ISSUES

Mapping an Issue provides a comprehensive structure for making decisions, solving problems, and resolving conflicts. Using this guide helps you to:

- Think systemically by incorporating the diverse interests of all SOS participants.
- Keep focus on the central issue.
- Include powerful emotions and wants (typically unacknowledged in many situations).
- Prevent the effects of partial information.
- Make the implicit, explicit and more resolvable.
- Generate congruent, effective solutions.
- Feel satisfied with both the process and the outcome.

This process incorporates all 11 talking and listening skills (in the SkillsZone) to help you and others work through an important issue in a collaborative way.

TIPS FOR FACILITATING THE PROCESS (When Others Do Not Know the Skills)

■ Be clear about your role as colleague, counselor, or facilitator. Clarify and gain others' approval for your role prior to your launching into the process.

■ Do not minimize or underplay the contract. Be sure to establish the details of an informal operating agreement.

■ (Optional) Overview what you are going to do — the Mapping process. Consider the usefulness of telling others at the outset (part of the contracting step, perhaps) that you are following a specific process. If your role is a colleague (peer), this may be particularly helpful. If however, it is as a counselor or facilitator (and everyone is clear about this role), most often you can lead people confidently through the process without outlining it beforehand. Usually they are not interested in how you proceed as long as the issue is resolved effectively.

■ Monitor each person's involvement (hot and cold) and contribution, as well as the overall progress of the process.

■ Watch readiness to move the process along (forward, by shifting to the next step, or occasionally backward, if an important step or information seems missing).

■ Adjust time in each step to be able to complete the entire process in the time allotted. If more time seems to be needed, Check Process, call Time Out, and re-schedule a time to complete the process.

APPLICATION: MAPPING AN ISSUE WITH OTHERS

Instructions

If you are in a situation with others where an issue is involved, and the others do not know the skills, you can apply the process. However, even before working through the steps, you must:

- Establish with the others your role as a colleague, coach, or facilitator.
- Remind yourself to stay in the SkillsZone as you monitor and go through the process.
- Proceed to:

Step 1. Identify and Define the Issue(s).

Step 2. Contract to Work Through the Issue.

- Consider using a flip chart to structure and record the process.

Proceed with the following steps when everyone is ready.

Step 3. Understand the Issue Completely

- Attend to hot and cold nonverbals and stop and shift as you watch the individual or the group as a whole.
- Encourage everyone to speak for themselves, if you hear them speaking for others.
- If there is considerable misunderstanding, or tension within those involved, encourage or direct various individuals to summarize each other's statements occasionally, before adding more information.

Step 4. Identify Wants for SOS.

- Help participants clearly distinguish and cover wants for SOS.

Step 5. Generate and Consider Options.

Step 6. Choose "Best Fir" Action(s).

Step 7. Test the Action Plan for "Best Fit" and Commitment.

Step 8. Implement Future Actions(s).

Step 9. Evaluate the Outcome.

MY USE OF MAPPING-AN-ISSUE PROCESS

Instructions

Rate your facility with the Mapping-an-Issue steps below:

		Special Strength	Okay As Is	Work Area
Step 1.	Identify and Define the Issue.	_____	_____	_____
Step 2.	Contract to Work Through the Issue.	_____	_____	_____
Step 3.	Understand the Issue Completely.	_____	_____	_____
Step 4.	Identify Wants for SOS.	_____	_____	_____
Step 5.	Generate and Consider Options.	_____	_____	_____
Step 6.	Choose Action(s).	_____	_____	_____
Step 7.	Test the Action Plan for "Best Fit" and Commitment.	_____	_____	_____
Step 8.	Implement Future Actions(s).	_____	_____	_____
Step 9.	Evaluate the Outcome.	_____	_____	_____

Action Plan

■ Circle two steps to improve.

Notes

10

PLANNING AN IMPORTANT CONVERSATION

**Analyze the Situation
Develop Your Plan
Anticipate the Unexpected**

When you know that you have an issue to resolve with someone and want a conversation about it to go well (even though you think it could be difficult), you can plan ahead of time for the interaction. This section will help you develop a process for such a situation.

The purpose of making and carrying out this plan is to help you (and whoever else is involved) feel satisfied with both the process of dealing with the issue and the outcome of it, whatever its content. Also, as you prepare for and then actually put your plan into effect, it is likely that you will gain more confidence in your use of these various aspects of communication.

The next page provides a list of the maps, skills, interactive guidelines, and processes in this CORE COMMUNICATION workbook. You can draw upon any of these as you construct your plan.

CORE COMMUNICATION MENU

Maps

- The SOS Network
- The Communication Styles
- Types of Issues
- The Awareness Wheel

- The Listening Cycle
- Conflict Processes
- The SkillsZone

Six Talking and Five Listening Skills

- Speak for Self
- Describe Sensory Data
- Express Thoughts
- Share Feelings
- Disclose Wants
- State Actions

- Attend: Look, Listen, Track
- Acknowledge Other's Experience
- Invite More Information
- Summarize to Ensure Accuracy
- Ask Open Questions

Interactive Guidelines

- Build and Maintain Rapport
- Watch the Hot and Cold Nonverbals
- Center and Breathe
- Expand Self Awareness
- Lead and Follow
- Ask yourself: "Is what I am doing working or not working?"
- Recognize, Stop, Center and Shift

Processes

- Responding to:
  - Resistance
  - Fight Talk
  - Spite Talk
- Mapping an Issue

PLAN A PROCESS

For this plan, choose an important, complicated, or stressful issue that you want to work out with one other person. (The general planning can also fit times for involving several people, but to make it manageable at this point, figure for just the two of you in the conversation.) Your task is to anticipate and prepare for a skilled conversation (with a caring attitude) with the person about the issue.

Four basic steps make up your plan. This is the overview.

Step 1. Do An Analysis.

- Figure out what the issue is and with whom; determine who else in the SOS system is involved.
- Clarify your awareness about the issue for yourself and the other person.

Step 2. Develop Your Interactional Plan.

- Determine how you will establish a "contract" with the other person for the conversation.
- Decide on the sequence of skills and processes you will use.
- Choose prompts to use.

Step 3. Anticipate the Unexpected and How You Will Respond.

- Ask yourself about what could go wrong in the interaction.
- Figure out how you will recover.

Step 4. Rehearse Your Process.

- Decide if this will be in front of others who know the skills and processes so you can receive coaching and feedback on your rehearsal.
- If you are alone, decide the method and tools you will use to step through the sequence.
- Go through the whole process, part by part.

Directions:

Use the worksheets below to analyze and plan your conversation.

Step 1. Do An Analysis.

- What is the issue?
- Who is the Other person?
- Besides you (Self) and the Other person, who are the Stakeholders?
- Fill out the Awareness Wheel below for yourself in relation to the issue.
- What awareness of yourself do you want to disclose to the other person, and in what sequence? (Number the parts in the order you wish to disclose. Start anywhere and go anywhere).

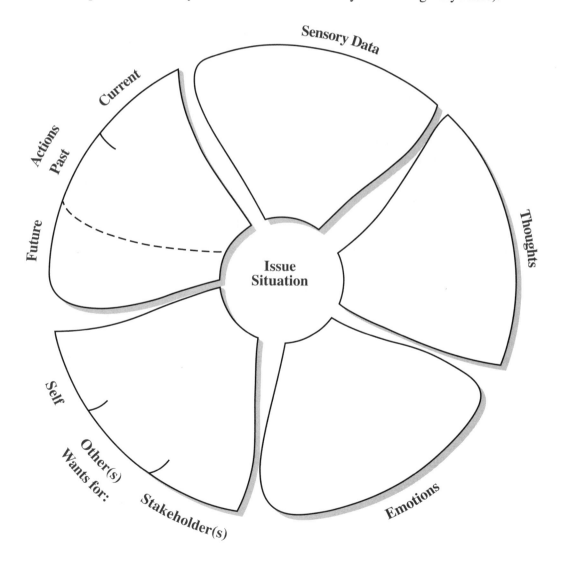

Stand in the Other Person's Shoes

- Stand in the Other person's shoes and fill out the Awareness Wheel as you think it is, from that person's perspective about the issue. To do this, recall what you have seen the other person do and heard him or her say. Add anything else that fits from other sensory data you have about the person.

- Look at both Wheels. What information seems particularly significant?

- What wants do you have in common that you are aware of now?

- What information is missing from the other person's Wheel (because you just do not know what it is)? Is this something to discover when you meet?

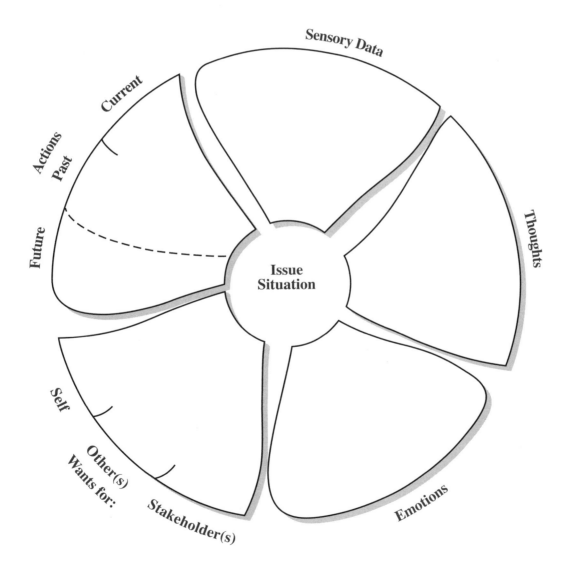

Step 2. Develop Your Interactional Plan.

■ Think about how to establish a contract for the conversation. Frame the conversation around SOS. For example, ask the other person if he or she would be willing to talk about an issue that is: bothering you, you believe is impacting him or her, and affecting the stakeholders.

■ Develop your sequence. Based on the Self and Other Awareness Wheels you have completed, how will you start the discussion? (For example, will you proceed by leading — sharing the zones of your Wheel in some particular order or by asking an open question? Or, will you proceed by following — inviting the other to talk?) List your anticipated sequence of processes and skills below: (Look on the Menu on page 184 for possibilities.)

1. _____

2. _____

3. _____

4. _____

5. _____

■ List anything particularly important to keep in mind for yourself in the situation that would help you (such as maps or guidelines).

■ List any prompts to use (Awareness Wheel pad, pocket cards, or laptop/tabletop mat).

Step 3. Anticipate How to Respond to the Unexpected.

Ask yourself:

■ What could go wrong in the interaction?

■ What might be the cues that things are not going right?

■ What might the person do to throw me off track?

■ What should I keep in mind that could help me (such as guidess I might let slip) to prevent this?

■ What are actions I can take to get back on track if things go wrong (for example, stop/shift, respond to resistance, breathe and center)? A list of possible actions includes:

_____

_____

_____

_____

Step 4. Rehearse Your Process.

■ If you are with others, who have learned CORE COMMUNICATION: MAPS, SKILLS AND PROCESSES, who can also serve as observer-coaches, share your plan with them. Let them know the issue, the intended sequence, and your set of actions if the conversation goes off track. Ask one of them to be a surrogate of the person you have the issue with, as you rehearse your process. The others in the group can be observers. Let them know if you want any coaching and, when you complete the rehearsal, any feedback.

■ If you are alone, use either the floor skills mats or laptop/tabletop mat to step through the sequence. Or, close your eyes and imagine yourself carrying out all parts of the process. When you run into difficulties as you imagine, then recall the actions to get you back on track.

In any case, stay in the SkillsZone:

■ Imagine yourself, managing yourself — staying in the SkillsZone being: **skilled, present, aware, centered and engaging** as you resolve the issue with the other person.

TAKE ACTION — CARRY OUT THE PROCESS.

AFTERWARDS: REFLECT ON HOW IT WENT

Instructions: Answer these questions:

1. What was the process like for you and for the other person?

2. What do you think you did well?

3. What could you improve?

4. What is your level of satisfaction (with the process, with the outcome)?

5. What do you think the level of satisfaction is for the other person and for any stakeholders?

HOW DO I COMMUNICATE?

Date _____

Instructions

Without reviewing how you marked your Pre-Questionnaire, follow the three steps below to assess how you are currently communicating, and to determine how well you have achieved your learning goals.

Step 1. Mark each item twice: first with an "X" to represent your typical behavior and again with an "O" to represent your more-so- or less-so desired behavior. If your typical and desired behaviors are the same, the "X" and "O" marks will be on the same number. If they are not the same, the marks will fall on different numbers.

In general, when you are discussing an important issue with someone, how often do you:

		Seldom Often	Difference
1.	Attempt to avoid the issue by joking or changing the subject?	1 2 3 4 5 6	___
2.	Listen briefly, then begin talking?	1 2 3 4 5 6	___
3.	Speak for other — put words into the other's mouth?	1 2 3 4 5 6	___
4.	Direct or instruct the other in what to do about it?	1 2 3 4 5 6	___
5.	Insist on "my way or the highway?"	1 2 3 4 5 6	___
6.	Blame or attack the other person directly?	1 2 3 4 5 6	___
7.	Make spiteful, undercutting remarks indirectly?	1 2 3 4 5 6	___
8.	Withhold or misrepresent information?	1 2 3 4 5 6	___
9.	Realize you are being ineffective?	1 2 3 4 5 6	___
10.	Calm yourself consciously when you feel tense or encounter tension in the other?	1 2 3 4 5 6	___
11.	Recognize what is going on inside yourself?	1 2 3 4 5 6	___
12.	Own your behavior — your contribution or response to situation?	1 2 3 4 5 6	___
13.	Describe your observations?	1 2 3 4 5 6	___
14.	Express your thoughts?	1 2 3 4 5 6	___
15.	Share your emotions?	1 2 3 4 5 6	___
16.	Disclose your wants and desires?	1 2 3 4 5 6	___
17.	Commit to future action(s)?	1 2 3 4 5 6	___

Post-Questionnaire

	Seldom	Often	Difference
18. Attend to the other's nonverbal responses?	1 2 3 4 5 6		___
19. Establish and maintain rapport?	1 2 3 4 5 6		___
20. Ask what is going on inside the other person?	1 2 3 4 5 6		___
21. Acknowledge the other's emotions?	1 2 3 4 5 6		___
22. Invite/encourage the other to talk?	1 2 3 4 5 6		___
23. Summarize the other's perspective accurately?	1 2 3 4 5 6		___
24. Identify clearly what the issue is before discussing it?	1 2 3 4 5 6		___
25. Propose a good time and place to discuss the issue?	1 2 3 4 5 6		___
26. Begin a discussion without considering the other's readiness?	1 2 3 4 5 6		___
27. Decide on a solution before fully understanding the issue?	1 2 3 4 5 6		___
28. Talk about the issue but leave it unresolved?	1 2 3 4 5 6		___
29. Give in to the other to keep the peace?	1 2 3 4 5 6		___
30. Follow an effective process for resolving issues?	1 2 3 4 5 6		___
31. Explore possible causes of the issue?	1 2 3 4 5 6		___
32. Brainstorm solutions to the issue?	1 2 3 4 5 6		___
33. Settle the issue by compromising — trading something for something?	1 2 3 4 5 6		___
34. Build in the wants and interests of the other?	1 2 3 4 5 6		___
35. Resolve the issue by building agreements collaboratively?	1 2 3 4 5 6		___
36. Make sure a solution to the issue fits well for everyone involved?	1 2 3 4 5 6		___

Total Difference Score ___

Step 2. When you have completed marking all the items, calculate the numerical difference between typical and desired scores for each item and record the results in the "difference" column. If the "X" and "O" are on the same number, the difference = 0. If the "X" is on 5 and the "O" is on 2, the difference = 3. Note the "O" can be located on a higher or lower number than the "X." Do not be concerned about the higher or lower direction of the scores, just calculate the numerical difference between the marks.

Step 3. Sum the difference scores.

(See the next page to review your skill learning.)

REVIEW MY LEARNING

When you have completed scoring your Post-Questionnaire, turn to your Pre-Questionnaire located in the front of the workbook, and look at the section where you listed your learning goals. Consider the following:

1. Determine how well you have achieved the learning goals you set for yourself.

2. Compare any changes in the "Total Difference Scores" between the Pre- and the Post-Questionnaire.

    A lower score (from Pre- to Post-Questionnaire) indicates that you have progressed closer to your desired skill use.

    A higher score (from Pre- to Post-Questionnaire) indicates that you have moved further away from your desired skill use.*

* If you have an increase in your Post-Questionnaire Difference Score from that of your Pre-Questionnaire, two reasons this can happen are: (1) You may be using more skills now, yet you also realize how much more effectively you could use the skills. In other words, your awareness has changed, and you have higher expectations of what skill use involves. (2) You may not have achieved the skill-learning progress you desired. If this is true, you may wish to consult with your CORE COMMUNICATION instructor about your results.

REFERENCES

M. Bear, B. Connors, and M. Paradiso, *Neuroscience: Exploring the Brain*, 2nd Edition, (Baltimore and Philadelphia: Lippincott Williams & Wilkins, 2001).

L. Cozolino, *The Neuroscience of Human Relationships: Attachment and the Developing Social Brain*, (New York and London: W.W. Norton & Company, 2006).

D. Goleman, *Social Intelligence: The New Science of Human Relationships*, (New York: Bantam Dell/Random House, 2006).

P. Lawson and R. Lindstrom, *Being Spherical: Reshaping Our Lives and Our World for the 21st Century*, (Evergreen, CO: Sphericity Press, 2004).

J. LeDoux, *The Emotional Brain: The Mysterious Underpinnings of Emotional Life*, (New York: Simon & Schuster, 1996).

C. Runde and T. Flanagan, *Becoming a Conflict Competent Leader,* (San Fancisco: Jossey-Bass, 2007).

C. Runde and T. Flanagan, *Developing Your Conflict Competence,* (San Fancisco: Jossey-Bass, 2010).

D. Siegel, *The Developing Mind: Toward a Neurobiology of Interpersonal Experience*, (New York: Guilford Publications, 1999).

ACKNOWLEDGEMENTS

We are grateful to Daniel Wackman, Ph.D. and the late Elam Nunnally, Ph.D., for their pioneering roles in the development and research of the ideas foundational to this workbook.

The revised Styles of Communication Map, featured in Chapter 1 and revisited throughout this workbook, grows out of the influence of Daniel Lord, Ph.D. We thank him for his significant contribution to this edition.

The impact of CORE COMMUNICATION on those who learn its concepts and skills depends heavily on the instructors who bring it to life. Special thanks go to these teachers/facilitators. Their valuable feedback and suggestions have been so important for this revision.

Over the years, students/participants have contacted us to tell of life-changing benefits they have received from applying the skills and processes of the material to their lives. Sometimes these are truly transformational. We appreciate hearing these experiences and recognize how encouraging they have been to us in our efforts for this edition.

ABOUT THE AUTHORS

Sherod Miller, Ph.D., is CEO of Interpersonal Communication Programs, Inc. (ICP) He is co-author of the earlier best sellers: *Alive and Aware*, *Straight Talk*, and *Connecting With Self and Others*. He is one of the originators of the Couple Communication Program. More recently, he has co-developed the *Becoming Conflict Competent* course for the Center for Conflict Dynamics at Eckerd College. He is a master facilitator for business and non-profit organizations, specializing in helping others learn and apply collaborative communication systems. He is a former Research Associate at the Family Study Center and faculty member in the Department of Medicine at the University of Minnesota. He has received four national awards for his research and teaching.

Phyllis A. Miller, Ph. D., is President of Interpersonal Communication Programs, Inc. (ICP) She is co-author of Couple Communication I *(Collaborative Marriage Skills)* and II *(Thriving Together in the SkillsZone)* and teaches instructor workshops for those programs. She has been on the staff at the University of Minnesota and at Augsburg College. At ICP she serves as editor and directs instructor certification for the various programs.